Target
Get back on track 5

AQA GCSE (9–1)
English Literature

Macbeth

David Grant

Pearson

Published by Pearson Education Limited, 80 Strand, London, WC2R ORL.
www.pearsonschoolsandfecolleges.co.uk

Text © Pearson Education Ltd 2017
Produced and typeset by Tech-Set Ltd, Gateshead

The right of David Grant to be identified as author of this work has been asserted by him in accordance with the Copyright, Designs and Patents Act 1988.

First published 2017

20 19 18 17
10 9 8 7 6 5 4 3 2 1

British Library Cataloguing in Publication Data
A catalogue record for this book is available from the British Library

ISBN 978 1 292 23008 5

Printed in Italy by LEGO S.p.A

Notes from the publisher
Pearson has robust editorial processes, including answer and fact checks, to ensure the accuracy of the content in this publication, and every effort is made to ensure this publication is free of errors. We are, however, only human, and occasionally errors do occur. Pearson is not liable for any misunderstandings that arise as a result of errors in this publication, but it is our priority to ensure that the content is accurate. If you spot an error, please do contact us at resourcescorrections@pearson.com so we can make sure it is corrected.

Contents

① Getting the plot straight

This unit will help you to understand and remember the plot of *Macbeth*. The skills you will build are to:

- remember the sequence of key events in the play
- understand the causes and consequences of the key events in the play
- understand what makes some events in the play more significant than others.

In the exam you will face questions like the one below. This is about the extract on the next page. At the end of the unit you will **plan your own response** to this question.

Before you tackle the question you will work through three key questions in the **skills boosts** to help you to get the plot of Macbeth straight.

① How do I make sure I know the plot?

② How can I explore the development of the plot?

③ How do I know which are the most significant events in the play?

Read the extract on the next page from Act 1 Scene 3 of *Macbeth*.

As you read, think about the following: ✓

Where in the play does this scene appear? Is it near the beginning, in the middle or at the end?

What has happened before this scene? What happens after this scene?

Why is the supernatural so important in this scene?

Exam-style question

Read the following extract from Act 1 Scene 3 of *Macbeth*.

At this point in the play Macbeth and Banquo are talking to three witches. The witches have just told Macbeth that he will become Thane of Cawdor and King of Scotland.

Extract A | Act 1 Scene 3 of *Macbeth*

MACBETH

Stay, you imperfect speakers, tell me more:
By Sinel's death I know I am Thane of Glamis;
But how of Cawdor? The Thane of Cawdor lives,
A prosperous gentleman; and to be king
5   Stands not within the prospect of belief,
No more than to be Cawdor. Say from whence
You owe this strange intelligence, or why
Upon this blasted heath you stop our way
With such prophetic greeting? Speak, I charge you.
Witches vanish

BANQUO

10   The earth hath bubbles, as the water has,
And these are of them. Whither are they vanish'd?

MACBETH

Into the air; and what seem'd corporal melted
As breath into the wind. Would they had stay'd!

BANQUO

Were such things here as we do speak about?
15   Or have we eaten on the insane root
That takes the reason prisoner?

MACBETH

Your children shall be kings.

BANQUO

You shall be king.

MACBETH

And Tw hane of Cawdor too: went it not so?

How do I make sure I know the plot?

One way to make sure you know the plot of *Macbeth* is to focus on some of the more memorable, key events that happen in the play.

Look at this list of characters in the play. Use it to help you answer the questions below.

Macbeth

Lady Macbeth

Seyton, Macbeth's servant

Banquo, a general

Fleance, his son

Macduff, Thane of Fife

Lady Macduff, his wife

Boy, son of Macduff

Duncan, King of Scotland

Malcolm, elder son of Duncan

Donalbain, younger son of Duncan

Duncan's guards

Hecate, queen of the witches

The three witches

Lennox, nobleman

Ross, nobleman

Menteith, nobleman

Angus, nobleman

Caithness, nobleman

Siward, Earl of Northumberland

Young Siward, his son

Two murderers

(1) Several characters die in the play. Cross ~~out~~ out all of the characters in the list above who die during the play.

(2) How many times does Macbeth meet the witches in the play? Circle Ⓐ the correct answer.

once   twice   three times

(3) **a** What is the first thing that happens in the play? Write ✏ your answer in box 1 of the plot summary below.

b What happens at the end of the play? Write ✏ your answer in box 12 below.

c Add ✏ Macbeth's meetings with the witches and all the deaths in the play to the plot summary below. Aim to get each meeting and each death in the correct order.   You might not fill every box.

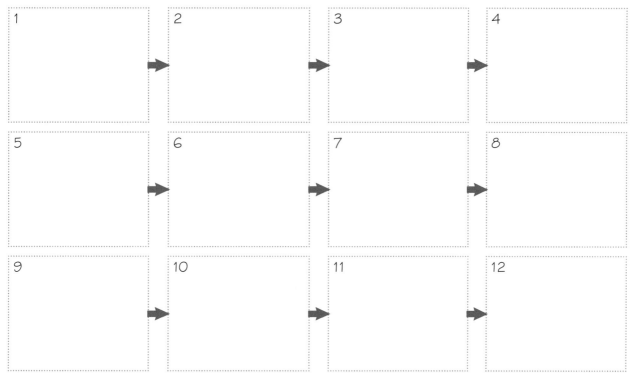

2 How can I explore the development of the plot?

Understanding the causes and consequences of key events in *Macbeth* will help you to get the plot straight and help you to understand how the plot develops.

Look at some of the key events in *Macbeth*.

Causes   Consequences

1.2 Macbeth fights bravely to repel the invading Norwegian army.

1.3 Macbeth and Banquo hear the witches' predictions: Macbeth will become Thane of Cawdor and King of Scotland.

1.4 Macbeth is made Thane of Cawdor.

1.5–1.7 Lady Macbeth persuades Macbeth to kill King Duncan.

2.2 Macbeth murders King Duncan.

2.4 Macbeth is King of Scotland.

3.3 Macbeth has Banquo murdered.

3.4 Macbeth sees Banquo's ghost at the feast to celebrate his coronation.

4.1 The witches reveal that 'no man born of woman shall harm Macbeth' and that he should 'Beware Macduff'.

4.2 Macbeth has Macduff's wife and children murdered.

5.1 Lady Macbeth's mind is troubled by her husband's actions.

5.5 Lady Macbeth dies.

5.8 Macduff kills Macbeth. Malcolm is made King of Scotland.

(1) One of the key events in the play is the **murder of King Duncan**.

   (a) On the left of the list above, draw arrows (↓) to show the chain of **causes** that leads to Macbeth **murdering King Duncan**.

   (b) On the right-hand side, draw arrows (↓) to show the chain of **consequences** caused by the **murder of King Duncan**.

One arrow for cause and one arrow for consequence have already been drawn for you to start the chain.

(2) Choose another significant event in the play and underline (A) it. Draw arrows (↓) in a different colour on the left-hand side to show the chain of events that **causes** it, and on the right-hand side to show the chain of **consequences** that follows it.

3 How do I know which are the most significant events in the play?

Understanding what each key event in the play contributes to the play will help you to get the plot straight and identify significant parts of the play to write about in your responses.

Look at some of the key events in *Macbeth*.

1.2 Macbeth fights bravely to repel the invading Norwegian army.	☐ ☐
1.3 Macbeth and Banquo hear the witches' predictions: Macbeth will become Thane of Cawdor and King of Scotland.	☐ ☐
1.4 Macbeth is made Thane of Cawdor.	☐ ☐
1.5–1.7 Lady Macbeth persuades Macbeth to kill King Duncan.	☐ ☐
2.2 Macbeth murders King Duncan.	☐ ☐
2.4 Macbeth is King of Scotland.	☐ ☐
3.3 Macbeth has Banquo murdered.	☐ ☐
3.4 Macbeth sees Banquo's ghost at the feast to celebrate his coronation.	☐ ☐
4.1 The witches reveal that 'no man born of woman shall harm Macbeth' and that he should 'Beware Macduff'.	☐ ☐
4.2 Macbeth has Macduff's wife and children murdered.	☐ ☐
5.1 Lady Macbeth's mind is troubled by her husband's actions.	☐ ☐
5.5 Lady Macbeth dies.	☐ ☐
5.8 Macduff kills Macbeth. Malcolm is made King of Scotland.	☐ ☐

(1) How would the story of *Macbeth* change if Shakespeare had decided to cut all the scenes featuring the witches? Write ✐ **one** or **two** sentences explaining how the story would change.

....

....

....

(2) Now, think carefully about each of the key events listed above. For each one, ask yourself:

? How would the plot be altered if it were removed?   ? How significant is it to the plot?

a Beside each key event, note down ✐ a mark out of 10: give it 1 out of 10 if it is not at all significant, 5 out of 10 if it is quite significant, and 10 out of 10 if it is very significant.

b Tick ✓ the **three** events that you have given the highest mark. Annotate ✐ each one, noting why you have decided it is so significant.

Getting the plot straight

To be sure of writing an effective response about *Macbeth*, you need to:

- know the key events in the play and the order in which they happen
- understand the causes and consequences of the key events in the play
- be able to identify the most significant events in the play and explain what makes them so significant.

Look again at the **first** part of the exam-style question you saw at the start of the unit.

Exam-style question

Starting with this extract, explain how far you think Shakespeare presents the supernatural as a powerful influence on the character of Macbeth.

Write about:

- how Shakespeare presents the influence of the supernatural on Macbeth in this speech

(1) Now look at one student's planning notes, written in response to this exam-style question.

> *Before this scene:* Macbeth is described as 'brave' by the Captain reporting the battle – 'well he deserves that name'.
>
> *After this scene:* Macbeth is plotting the murder of Duncan to make sure the witches' prediction comes true.
>
> So the supernatural has a big influence on Macbeth in this scene, turning him from hero to traitor.
>
> *In the extract:*
> He shows some doubt: 'to be king/Stands not within the prospect of belief'.
> He clearly believes the witches – 'stay you imperfect speakers' – wants to hear more.
> He calls their news 'intelligence', suggesting he thinks it is fact.
> And neither Macbeth nor Banquo shows any doubt when they sum up the predictions: 'You (shall) be king.'

Think about all the ideas this student has included in their plan. Annotate ✏ their plan, highlighting all the different elements that will make their response to the first part of the question above successful.

Your turn!

After you have read and understood the text, identified its key points and explored the writer's intention, you are ready to tackle **all of the questions** you are likely to be asked in your exam.

You are now going to **plan your own answer** in response to the exam-style question.

Exam-style question

Starting with this extract, explain how far you think Shakespeare presents the supernatural as a powerful influence on the character of Macbeth.

Write about:

- how Shakespeare presents the influence of the supernatural on Macbeth in this speech
- how Shakespeare presents the influence of the supernatural on Macbeth in the play as a whole.

1 Look again at some of the key events in the play.

Event	✓	✗
1.2 Macbeth fights bravely to repel the invading Norwegian army.		
1.3 Macbeth and Banquo hear the witches' predictions: Macbeth will become Thane of Cawdor and King of Scotland.		
1.4 Macbeth is made Thane of Cawdor.		
1.5–1.7 Lady Macbeth persuades Macbeth to kill King Duncan.		
2.2 Macbeth murders King Duncan.		
2.4 Macbeth is King of Scotland.		
3.3 Macbeth has Banquo murdered.		
3.4 Macbeth sees Banquo's ghost at the feast to celebrate his coronation.		
4.1 The witches reveal that 'no man born of woman shall harm Macbeth' and that he should 'Beware Macduff'.		
4.2 Macbeth has Macduff's wife and children murdered.		
5.1 Lady Macbeth's mind is troubled by her husband's actions.		
5.5 Lady Macbeth dies.		
5.8 Macduff kills Macbeth. Malcolm is made King of Scotland.		

a Which key events include elements of the supernatural? Tick ✓ them.

b Which of these elements of the supernatural have a significant influence on Macbeth? Add another ✓ to the box.

c Which key events show the influence on the supernatural on Macbeth? Underline Ⓐ the scene numbers.

d Think about the other side of the argument: which key events show Macbeth being influenced in other ways or making choices that are **not** influenced by the supernatural? Cross ✗ them.

e Which are the most significant scenes you would choose to write about in your response to the exam-style question above? Circle Ⓐ the scene numbers.

Review your skills

Check up

Review your plan for the exam-style question on page 7. Tick ✓ the column to show how well you think you have done each of the following.

	Not quite ✓	Nearly there ✓	Got it! ✓
identified the key events in the play that include elements of the supernatural	☐	☐	☐
thought about key events in the play that show the influence of the supernatural on Macbeth's actions	☐	☐	☐
thought about key events in the play that show Macbeth making choices that are not influenced by the supernatural	☐	☐	☐

Look over all of your work in this unit. Note down ✏ the **three** most important things to remember when planning your response to a *Macbeth* question.

1. ....
2. ....
3. ....

Need more practice?

Here is another exam-style question, this time relating to the extract from Act 1 Scene 2 on page 73 (Extract A).

Exam-style question

Starting with this extract, explain how far you think Shakespeare presents Macbeth as a ruthless and violent man.

Write about:

- how Shakespeare presents Macbeth in this extract
- how Shakespeare presents Macbeth in the play as a whole.

(30 marks)
AO4 (4 mark)

Which key events in the play would you choose to write ✏ about in your response to this question? You'll find some suggested ideas in the Answers section.

How confident do you feel about each of these **skills?** Colour ✏ in the bars.

1 How do I make sure I know the plot?

2 How can I explore the development of the plot?

3 How do I know which are the most significant events in the play?

② Analysing the extract

This unit will help you to explore the extract in the *Macbeth* exam question. The skills you will build are to:

- select relevant points to make in your analysis
- develop your analysis
- structure your analysis.

In the exam you will face questions like the one below. This is about the extract on the next page. At the end of the unit you will **write one paragraph** in response to this question, **focusing on the extract.**

> **Exam-style question**
>
> Starting with this extract, explain how far you think Shakespeare presents power, and the desire for power, as destructive.
>
> Write about:
>
> - how Shakespeare presents power and the desire for power in this extract
> - how Shakespeare presents power and the desire for power in the play as a whole.
>
> (30 marks)
> AO4 (4 marks)

Before you tackle the question you will work through three key questions in the **skills boosts** to help you analyse the extract.

① How do I choose the points I need to make? **② How do I develop my analysis?** **③ How do I structure a paragraph of analysis?**

Read the extract on the next page from Act 1 Scene 4 of *Macbeth*.

As you read, think about the following:

What has happened before this scene? What happens after this scene?

How does Shakespeare present Duncan in this extract?

How does Shakespeare present Macbeth in this extract?

Read the following extract from Act 1 Scene 4 of *Macbeth*.

At this point in the play, Duncan is thanking Macbeth and Banquo for their part in the victory over the invading Norwegian army. The Thane of Cawdor has been hanged for treachery and Macbeth has been given his title, just as the witches predicted.

Extract A | Act 1 Scene 4 of *Macbeth*

MACBETH
The service and the loyalty I owe,
In doing it, pays itself. Your Highness' part
Is to receive our duties; and our duties
Are to your throne and state, children and servants,
5   Which do but what they should, by doing every thing
Safe toward your love and honour.
DUNCAN
          Welcome hither:
I have begun to plant thee, and will labour
To make thee full of growing. Noble Banquo,
10   That hast no less deserved, nor must be known
No less to have done so. Let me infold thee
And hold thee to my heart.
BANQUO
          There if I grow,
The harvest is your own.
DUNCAN
15   My plenteous joys,
Wanton in fulness, seek to hide themselves
In drops of sorrow. Sons, kinsmen, Thanes,
And you whose places are the nearest, know
We will establish our estate upon
20   Our eldest, Malcolm, whom we name hereafter
The Prince of Cumberland; which honour must
Not unaccompanied invest him only,
But signs of nobleness, like stars, shall shine
On all deservers. From hence to Inverness,
25   And bind us further to you.
MACBETH
The rest is labour, which is not used for you:
I'll be myself the harbinger and make joyful
The hearing of my wife with your approach;
So humbly take my leave.
DUNCAN
30   My worthy Cawdor!
MACBETH:
[Aside] The Prince of Cumberland! That is a step
On which I must fall down, or else o'erleap,
For in my way it lies. Stars, hide your fires;
Let not light see my black and deep desires.
35   The eye wink at the hand; yet let that be,
Which the eye fears, when it is done, to see.

How do I choose the points I need to make?

The first thing you need to do is to identify which parts of the extract you can explore further in your response to the question.

Look again at the exam-style question you are exploring.

Exam-style question

Starting with this extract, explain how far you think Shakespeare presents power, and the desire for power, as destructive.

1. Now look through the extract on page 10, focusing on each speech in turn:

1. | Macbeth expresses his loyalty and duty to King Duncan [lines 1–6]

2. | Duncan welcomes and praises Macbeth and Banquo [lines 7–12]

3. | Banquo expresses his thanks and loyalty to Duncan [lines 13–14]

4. | Duncan reveals that his son, Malcolm, will be king after him [lines 15–25]

5. | Macbeth will tell his wife that Duncan will be staying at their castle [26–29]

6. | Macbeth thinks he will have to remove Malcolm if he wants to be king [lines 31–36]

a Decide which **three** speeches reveal the most about how Shakespeare presents power and the desire for power. Label 🖉 them A, B and C.

Think about:
- how Duncan uses his power and how he acts as king
- what Macbeth says to Duncan, then compare it with what Macbeth says to himself.

b Note 🖉 below what each of the speeches you have chosen reveals about how Shakespeare presents power and the desire for power.

A

B

C

2 How do I develop my analysis?

To develop your analysis, you need to think about what the characters say, why they say it, and what this reveals about the aspect of the play that you are exploring. Your ideas need to be supported by evidence from the extract.

Look again at the exam-style question you are exploring.

Exam-style question

Starting with this extract, explain how far you think Shakespeare presents power, and the desire for power, as destructive.

(1) Now look at one speech from the extract that reveals something about power and the desire for power.

> **DUNCAN**
> Welcome hither:
> I have begun to plant thee, and will labour
> To make thee full of growing. Noble Banquo,
> That hast no less deserved, nor must be known
> No less to have done so. Let me infold thee
> And hold thee to my heart.

Banquo and Macbeth have just won a great victory for Duncan and kept his kingdom safe from the invading Norwegian army.

a What does Duncan say in this speech? Sum it up in a **few** words.

....

b Why is Duncan saying this? Write one or **two** sentences explaining your ideas.

....

....

....

c Look again at your answers above. What does Duncan's speech suggest about power and the desire for power?

....

....

....

d Which lines show this most clearly? Choose **two** short quotations and underline Ⓐ them.

(2) Now choose another speech from the extract that reveals something about power and/or the desire for power.

a Annotate the text on page 10, noting down:
- what the character says
- why they say it
- what it reveals about power and/or the desire for power.

b Then underline Ⓐ **two** short quotations to support your ideas.

3 How do I structure a paragraph of analysis?

Each paragraph of your analysis should include:
- a key point focusing on the key words in the question
- evidence from the text to support your point
- comments on the evidence and its impact
- a response to the question.

You can build your skill in analysing the extract in more depth and detail in Unit 3.

Look at the sentences from one paragraph of a student's response to this exam-style question.

Exam-style question

Starting with this extract, explain how far you think Shakespeare presents power, and the desire for power, as destructive.

(1) Tick ✓ the sentences you would include in a paragraph in response to the exam-style question.

		✓	✐
A	King Duncan is presented as warm, generous and grateful for Macbeth and Banquo's victory over the Norwegian army.		
B	Duncan uses his power in a positive way, rewarding his people for their help and support.		
C	Duncan tells Macbeth that he will 'labour / To make thee full of growing', suggesting that Duncan will reward him with more honours and titles if he remains loyal and fights hard for Duncan.		
D	Duncan calls Banquo 'Noble' and embraces him: 'Let me infold thee / And hold thee to my heart', suggesting he feels respect and affection for him.		
E	Shakespeare does not always present power as destructive in 'Macbeth'.		
F	Power can be constructive, not destructive, if the king does not take his power, and the people he has power over, for granted.		

(2) How would you sequence your chosen sentences in a paragraph? Number ✐ them.

(3) Write ✐ a paragraph on paper using your chosen sentences and linking them with some or all of the following phrases.

Similarly	This shows that	It suggests that	For example,	It could be argued that

(4) Look at the sentences you have chosen and sequenced.

   (a) Which sentences make a key point? Label ✐ them 'Key point'.

   (b) Which support a key point using evidence? Label ✐ them 'Evidence'.

   (c) Which comment on the evidence and its impact? Label ✐ them 'Comment'.

   (d) Which show the writer's response to the question? Label ✐ them 'Response'.

Analysing the extract

To analyse the extract effectively, you need to:

- identify the parts of the extract that are relevant to the question
- explore what these parts suggest about the focus of the question
- structure your paragraphs of analysis to include a key point supported by evidence, a comment on its impact and a response to the question.

Look at the exam-style question you saw at the start of the unit.

Exam-style question

Starting with this extract, explain how far you think Shakespeare presents power, and the desire for power, as destructive.

① Look at this paragraph, taken from a student's response to this question. It focuses on the extract on page 10, Extract A.

> In this extract, King Duncan appears to be a good leader, using his power to reward those who are loyal to him and fight for him. Macbeth has returned victorious from battle, and has been rewarded for his loyalty with the title of Thane of Cawdor. Duncan seems to promise that Macbeth will continue to be rewarded more if he continues to please Duncan: 'I have begun to plant thee, and will labour / To make thee full of growing.' While this seems to be a perfect picture of a loyal subject and a grateful king, it could be argued that Duncan is bribing Macbeth with the title of Thane of Cawdor to make sure he stays loyal. Furthermore, this extract comes just after Duncan has had the previous Thane of Cawdor executed for treachery. So this part of the play suggests that, in order to keep power, you must repay loyalty, but be cruel and ruthless when your power is challenged.

   a Which of the following has this student achieved? Tick ✓ them.

      A Identified a part of the extract that is relevant to the question. ☐

      B Explored what it suggests about the focus of the question. ☐

      C Made a key point. ☐

      D Supported it with evidence. ☐

      E Commented on its impact. ☐

      F Responded to the question. ☐

   b Highlight ✎ and label ✎ where in the paragraph this student has achieved C, D, E and F.

Your turn!

You are now going to **write one or two paragraphs** in response to the exam-style question below, **focusing on Macbeth's first and last speeches** in Extract A on page 10.

First speech	Last speech
MACBETH The service and the loyalty I owe, In doing it, pays itself. Your Highness' part Is to receive our duties; and our duties Are to your throne and state, children and servants, Which do but what they should, by doing every thing Safe toward your love and honour.	**MACBETH:** *[Aside]* The Prince of Cumberland! That is a step On which I must fall down, or else o'erleap, For in my way it lies. Stars, hide your fires; Let not light see my black and deep desires. The eye wink at the hand; yet let that be, Which the eye fears, when it is done, to see.

Exam-style question

Starting with this extract, explain how far you think Shakespeare presents power, and the desire for power, as destructive.

Write about:

- how Shakespeare presents power and the desire for power in this extract
- how Shakespeare presents power and the desire for power in the play as a whole. **(30 marks)**

AO4 (4 marks)

(1) Look at Macbeth's first speech. What does this suggest about Macbeth's attitude to power? 🖉

First speech

(2) Look at Macbeth's last speech. What does this suggest about Macbeth's attitude to power? 🖉

Second speech

(3) Think about both of Macbeth's speeches. How is Shakespeare presenting power and the desire for power here? 🖉

You may want to use some of the ideas below, or use your own.

destructive	dangerous	dishonest
damaging	fragile	corrupting

How is power presented?

(4) Underline Ⓐ short, relevant quotations in the speeches above that you can use in your response.

(5) On paper, write 🖉 **one** or **two** paragraphs in response to the exam-style question above.

Review your skills

Check up

Review your response to the exam-style question on page 15. Tick ⊘ the column to show how well you think you have done each of the following.

	Not quite ⊘	Nearly there ⊘	Got it! ⊘
made a relevant key point	☐	☐	☐
supported my key point with relevant evidence	☐	☐	☐
commented on the impact of my evidence	☐	☐	☐
responded to the question	☐	☐	☐

Need more practice?

Here is another exam-style question, this time relating to the extract from Act 1 Scene 2 on page 73 (Extract A).

Exam-style question

Starting with this extract, explain how far you think Shakespeare presents Macbeth as a ruthless and violent man.

Write about:

• how Shakespeare presents Macbeth in this extract
• how Shakespeare presents Macbeth in the play as a whole.

(30 marks)
AO4 (4 marks)

Write ⊘ **one** or **two** paragraphs in response to this question, focusing on the extract only.

You'll find some suggested ideas in the Answers section.

How confident do you feel about each of these **skills**? Colour ⊘ in the bars.

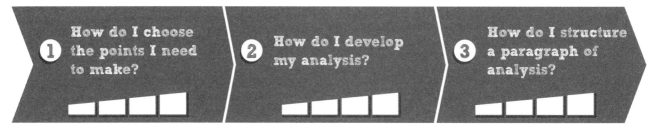

1 How do I choose the points I need to make?

2 How do I develop my analysis?

3 How do I structure a paragraph of analysis?

③ Commenting on the writer's choices in the extract

This unit will help you to comment on Shakespeare's choices in the extract from *Macbeth*. The skills you will build are to:

• identify relevant language choices to comment on

• identify relevant structural choices to comment on

• make effective comments on the writer's choices.

In the exam you will face questions like the one below. This is about the extract on the next page. At the end of the unit you will **write one or two paragraphs** in response to this question, **focusing on the extract**.

Exam-style question

Starting with this extract, explain how far you think Shakespeare presents Lady Macbeth as a more ruthless and ambitious person than Macbeth.

Write about:

• how Shakespeare presents Lady Macbeth as ruthless and ambitious in this extract

• how Shakespeare presents Lady Macbeth in the play as a whole.

(30 marks)

AO4 (4 marks)

Before you tackle the question you will work through three key questions in the **skills boosts** to help you comment on the writer's choices in the extract.

 ① How do I identify significant language choices?

 ② How do I identify significant structural choices?

 ③ How do I comment on the writer's choices?

Read the extract on the next page from Act 1 Scene 5 of *Macbeth*.

As you read, think about the following:

What has happened before this scene? What happens after this scene?	How does Shakespeare present Lady Macbeth in this extract?	How does Shakespeare present Macbeth in this extract?
☐	☐	☐

Exam-style question

Read the following extract from Act 1 Scene 5 of *Macbeth*.

At this point in the play, Lady Macbeth has learned of the witches' predictions: Macbeth will be king. She knows that her husband is ambitious and she has resolved to persuade him to kill King Duncan. Macbeth returns home and tells his wife that the king will be staying with them that night.

Extract A | Act 1 Scene 5 of *Macbeth*

Enter MACBETH

LADY MACBETH
      Great Glamis! worthy Cawdor!
Greater than both, by the all-hail hereafter!
Thy letters have transported me beyond
This ignorant present, and I feel now
5   The future in the instant.
MACBETH
      My dearest love,
Duncan comes here tonight.
LADY MACBETH
      And when goes hence?
MACBETH
      Tomorrow, as he purposes.
LADY MACBETH
10   O, never
Shall sun that morrow see!
Your face, my Thane, is as a book where men
May read strange matters. To beguile the time,
Look like the time; bear welcome in your eye,
15   Your hand, your tongue: look like the innocent flower,
But be the serpent under't. He that's coming
Must be provided for: and you shall put
This night's great business into my dispatch;
Which shall to all our nights and days to come
20   Give solely sovereign sway and masterdom.
MACBETH
      We will speak further.
LADY MACBETH
      Only look up clear;
To alter favour ever is to fear:
Leave all the rest to me.
Exeunt

How do I identify significant language choices?

The language that Shakespeare gives each character in a scene or extract can reveal a great deal about their thoughts, motivations and relationships.

1 Look at the lines that Shakespeare gives Lady Macbeth at the start of Extract A on page 18.

Lady Macbeth

> Great Glamis! worthy Cawdor!
> Greater than both, by the all-hail hereafter!

a In this speech, Lady Macbeth is both flattering Macbeth and reminding him that he could be king. Which words make this clearest? Circle Ⓐ **one** or **two** that are most significant.

b What does Shakespeare's choice of these words or phrases suggest about the character of Lady Macbeth and/or her relationship with Macbeth? Write ✎ **one** or **two** sentences summing up your ideas.

....

....

....

2 Now look at two more extracts from Lady Macbeth's speeches in the extract below.

a Annotate ✎ each speech, noting your thoughts on these questions:

   i What does Lady Macbeth say in this speech?

   ii Why is Lady Macbeth saying this?

b Which **one** or **two** words or phrases in the speech highlight or emphasise what she is saying and the reason she is saying it most clearly? Circle Ⓐ them.

c What does each word or phrase you have circled suggest about the character of Lady Macbeth and/or her relationship with Macbeth? Annotate ✎ the words and phrases you have circled.

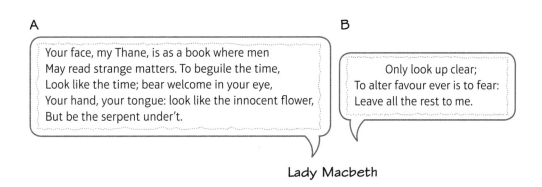

A

> Your face, my Thane, is as a book where men
> May read strange matters. To beguile the time,
> Look like the time; bear welcome in your eye,
> Your hand, your tongue: look like the innocent flower,
> But be the serpent under't.

B

> Only look up clear;
> To alter favour ever is to fear:
> Leave all the rest to me.

Lady Macbeth

2 How do I identify significant structural choices?

When you think about Shakespeare's structural choices, think about how actors might perform the lines, and the impression this might create for the audience.

1 Look at these lines from the extract.

> **MACBETH**
>   My dearest love,
> Duncan comes here tonight.
> **LADY MACBETH**
>   And when goes hence?
> **MACBETH**
> Tomorrow, as he purposes.

a How would you describe the mood of this conversation? Circle Ⓐ **one** or **two** of the ideas below, or add 🖉 your own.

tense	dramatic	excited	nervous	awkward	hurried

....

....

b How does the **length** of the lines, and the **pace** at which the actors might deliver them, contribute to this mood? Write 🖉 **one** or **two** sentences explaining your ideas.

....

....

....

2 Now look at the whole extract.

a Which character has the most lines? Cross out ⊖ all or part of the sentences below to sum up your ideas.

   i   Lady Macbeth / Macbeth says much less than Lady Macbeth / Macbeth.

   ii Lady Macbeth / Macbeth does most of the talking.

   iii The two characters have a similar amount of lines.

b Look at your answer to question **2** **a** above. What does this suggest about:

   • Macbeth's character, how he is feeling, and his relationship with his wife

   • Lady Macbeth's character, how she is feeling, and her relationship with her husband?

   Write 🖉 **one** or **two** sentences, summing up your ideas.

....

....

③ How do I comment on the writer's choices?

An effective comment on the writer's choices highlights the **choice** the writer has made, and comments on its **effect**.

Look at some of the different kinds of comment on **language** and **structure** you could make on Lady Macbeth's final line from Extract A on page 18.

> Leave all the rest to me.

Lady Macbeth

Language

You can comment on...   choice   +   effect

- the kind of language in the whole quotation

| Simple, monosyllabic language | suggests her blunt, forceful tone. | ☐ |

- a specific type of word

| The imperative verb 'Leave' | shows her dominance over Macbeth. | ☐ |

- the connotations or implications of a specific word or phrase.

| The phrase 'the rest' | suggests she is taking control of almost all of the plan to kill Duncan. | ☐ |

Structure

You can comment on...   choice   +   effect

- the line's position in the scene

| This is the final line of the scene | suggesting that Lady Macbeth gets the last word in this discussion. | ☐ |

- the length of the line(s)

| This short line | suggests an emphatic, unarguable tone. | ☐ |

- the order of the words or ideas in the line(s).

| The final word of this line, 'me', | suggests that Lady Macbeth is in control. | ☐ |

① Which of these would you include in your comments? Tick ✓ them.

② Now think about another part of Lady Macbeth's speech.

> look like the innocent flower,
> But be the serpent under't.

Think about: how Shakespeare uses **contrast** to structure these lines.

Write 🖉 **one** or **two** sentences commenting on Shakespeare's choices of language and structure in this section.

....

....

....

Commenting on the writer's choices in the extract

To comment effectively on Shakespeare's choices in the extract, you need to:

- identify relevant evidence from the extract to support your ideas
- select significant language and/or structural choices in the evidence you have identified
- highlight in your evidence the choices that Shakespeare has made and comment on their effect.

(For more help on structuring a paragraph of analysis, see Unit 2.)

Look at this exam-style question you saw at the start of the unit on page 17.

Exam-style question

Starting with this extract, explain how far you think Shakespeare presents Lady Macbeth as a more ruthless and ambitious person than Macbeth.

(1) Can you identify all the different things the student has included in this paragraph?
Link ✐ the annotations to the paragraph to show where the student has included them.

Key features of an effective paragraph of analysis:

key point focusing on the key words in the question

evidence from the text to support the point

comments on the evidence and its impact

a response to the question

As soon as Macbeth appears at the start of the extract, Lady Macbeth ruthlessly dominates the scene and tries to influence him. She welcomes him home, calling him 'Great Glamis! worthy Cawdor!' These short, emphatic exclamations suggest her excitement and are meant to flatter Macbeth. She uses the positive adjectives 'great' and 'worthy' to boost his confidence and make him feel important. She also uses his new title of 'Cawdor' to remind him of the witches' prediction that has already come true, and the rest of the prediction which she wants him to make come true. Lady Macbeth doubts her husband will be ruthless enough to do this, and so feels she must flatter and manipulate him to be as ruthless and ambitious as she is.

Key features of an effective comment on the writer's choices:

a comment on language choice(s)

a comment on structural choice(s)

Your turn!

You are now going to **write one or two paragraphs** in response to the exam-style question below, **focusing on Extract A on page 18.**

focusing on Extract A on page 18.

Exam-style question

Starting with this extract, explain how far you think Shakespeare presents Lady Macbeth as a more ruthless and ambitious person than Macbeth.

Write about:

- how Shakespeare presents Lady Macbeth as ruthless and ambitious in this extract
- how Shakespeare presents Lady Macbeth in the play as a whole.

(30 marks)

AO4 (4 marks)

(1) What do you think? Is Lady Macbeth presented as a more ruthless and ambitious person than Macbeth? Write ✐ **one** sentence summing up your response.

....

....

(2) Focus on **one** speech in the extract that supports your answer to question **(1)** above. Circle Ⓐ it on page 18.

(3) Now look closely at the speech you have chosen. Select a short quotation that clearly supports your answer to question **(1)** above. Underline Ⓐ it on page 18.

(4) Think about words or phrases in your chosen quotation that make a significant contribution to your answer to question **(1)** above.

   a Which words or phrases reveal something significant about the character, their thoughts, attitudes or relationships? Circle Ⓐ them on page 18.

   b What do those words and phrases suggest about this character? Annotate ✐ them.

(5) Now think about Shakespeare's structural choices in your chosen quotation. Think about:

- the line's position in the scene
- the length of the line(s)
- the order of the words or ideas in the line(s).

Do Shakespeare's structural choices in your chosen quotation make a significant contribution to your answer to question **(1)** above? How? Annotate ✐ your chosen quotation with your ideas.

(6) Using all the ideas you have noted, write ✐ **one** paragraph on paper in response to the exam-style question above.

(7) Repeat questions **(2)**–**(6)**, focusing on a different speech from the extract. ✐

Review your skills

Check up

Review your response to the exam-style question on page 23. Tick ✓ the column to show how well you think you have done each of the following.

	Not quite ✓	Nearly there ✓	Got it! ✓
structured an effective paragraph of analysis in response to the question	☐	☐	☐
commented on Shakespeare's language choices	☐	☐	☐
commented on Shakespeare's structural choices	☐	☐	☐

Need more practice?

Here is another exam-style question, this time relating to the extract from Act 3 Scene 1 on page 74 (Extract B).

Exam-style question

Starting with this extract, explain how far you think Shakespeare explores the consequences of dishonesty and deception in *Macbeth*.

Write about:

• how Shakespeare presents Banquo and Macbeth as dishonest and deceitful in this extract

• how Shakespeare presents the consequences of dishonesty and deception in the play as a whole.

(30 marks)

AO4 (4 marks)

Write 🖉 **one** or **two** paragraphs in response to this question, focusing on the extract only.

You'll find some suggested ideas in the Answers section.

How confident do you feel about each of these **skills**? Colour 🖉 in the bars.

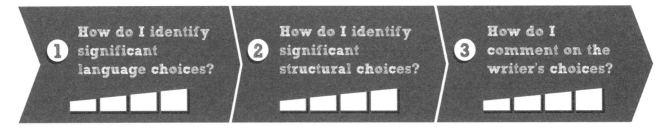

1 How do I identify significant language choices?

2 How do I identify significant structural choices?

3 How do I comment on the writer's choices?

Exploring themes and characters

This unit will help you to explore how the characters and themes of *Macbeth* develop in the play, and help you to develop your response to them. The skills you will build are to:

- track how characters develop in the play
- track how themes develop in the play
- comment on the development of characters and themes in the play.

In the exam you will face questions like the one below. This is about the extract on the next page. At the end of the unit you will **plan and write one or two paragraphs** in response to this question.

> ### Exam-style question
>
> Starting with this extract, explore how Shakespeare presents good and evil in the play.
>
> Write about:
> - how Shakespeare presents Macbeth and Lady Macbeth as good or evil in this extract
> - how Shakespeare presents good and evil in the play as a whole.
>
> (30 marks)
>
> AO4 (4 marks)

Before you tackle the question you will work through three key questions in the **skills boosts** to help you explore the play's themes and characters.

 1 How do I track the development of a character?

 2 How do I track the development of a theme?

 3 How do I comment on the development of character or theme?

Read the extract on the next page from Act 1 Scene 7 of *Macbeth*.

As you read, think about the following:

| What has happened before this scene? What happens after this scene? | How does Shakespeare present Lady Macbeth in this extract? | How does Shakespeare present Macbeth in this extract? |

Exam-style question

Read the following extract from Act 1 Scene 7 of *Macbeth*.

At this point in the play, Duncan is staying in Macbeth's castle. Macbeth has realised how wrong and how risky it would be to murder Duncan and has decided that he cannot do it.

Extract A | Act 1 Scene 7 of *Macbeth*

MACBETH

We will proceed no further in this business:
He hath honour'd me of late; and I have bought
Golden opinions from all sorts of people,
Which would be worn now in their newest gloss,
5   Not cast aside so soon.

LADY MACBETH

Was the hope drunk
Wherein you dress'd yourself? Hath it slept since?
And wakes it now, to look so green and pale
At what it did so freely? From this time
10   Such I account thy love. Art thou afeard
To be the same in thine own act and valour
As thou art in desire? Wouldst thou have that
Which thou esteem'st the ornament of life,
And live a coward in thine own esteem,
15   Letting 'I dare not' wait upon 'I would,'
Like the poor cat i' the adage?

MACBETH

Prithee, peace:
I dare do all that may become a man;
Who dares do more is none.

LADY MACBETH

20   What beast was't, then,
That made you break this enterprise to me?
When you durst do it, then you were a man;
And, to be more than what you were, you would
Be so much more the man. Nor time nor place
25   Did then adhere, and yet you would make both:
They have made themselves, and that their fitness now
Does unmake you. I have given suck, and know
How tender 'tis to love the babe that milks me:
I would, while it was smiling in my face,
30   Have pluck'd my nipple from his boneless gums,
And dash'd the brains out, had I so sworn as you
Have done to this.

MACBETH

If we should fail?

LADY MACBETH

We fail!
35   But screw your courage to the sticking-place,
And we'll not fail.

How do I track the development of a character?

The key characters in the play are Macbeth and Lady Macbeth. To write effectively about them in the play as a whole, you need to think about how Shakespeare's presentation of them changes as the action of the play develops.

(1) Think about how Macbeth is presented at the **start** of the play.
In **Act 1**:

- we hear about 'brave Macbeth' in battle in Act 1 Scene 2

- he hears the witches' predictions in Act 1 Scene 3

- in Act 1 Scene 4, he swears loyalty to Duncan while hiding his 'deep and dark desires'

- he fears his ambition and is reluctant to kill Duncan in Act 1 Scenes 5 and 7

How would you sum up the character of Macbeth at the start of the play? Tick ✓ any of the words below and/or add 🖉 your own idea.

brave	loyal	dishonest	ruthless	ambitious	superstitious	manipulative	frightened	
☐	☐	☐	☐	☐	☐	☐	☐	

(2) Now think about Macbeth at the **end** of the play. In **Act 5**:

- after meeting the witches in Act 4, he believes he is invincible

- in Act 5 Scene 3, he does not seem surprised or upset at Lady Macbeth's death and has 'almost forgot the taste of fears'

- he is killed by Macduff in Act 5 scene 8

How would you sum up the character of Macbeth at the end of the play? Note 🖉 up to **five** words.

Look at the words you chose to describe him in question **(1)**. What has changed?

....

(3) Now look at some of the key scenes showing the development of the character of Macbeth.

| 2.2 | Macbeth murders King Duncan. He fears he shall 'sleep no more'. | /10 |

| 3.4 | Macbeth sees Banquo's ghost. Macbeth says he is 'in blood/ Stepped in so far that, should I wade no more./Returning were as tedious as go o'er.' | /10 |

| 3.2 | Macbeth tells his wife that his mind is 'full of scorpions' but not that he has arranged Banquo's murder. | /10 |

| 4.2 | Macbeth has Macduff's wife and children murdered. | /10 |

| 3.3 | Macbeth has Banquo murdered. | /10 |

a How significant is each of these scenes in showing the change in Macbeth's character from the start to the end of the play? Give 🖉 each one a mark out of ten: 1/10 = not at all significant; 10/10 = highly significant.

b Write 🖉 **one** or **two** sentences summing up how the character of Macbeth develops and changes during the course of the play.

....

....

Unit 4 Exploring themes and characters   **27**

2 How do I track the development of a theme?

To track the way in which Shakespeare explores a theme of the play, you need to identify key scenes in which that theme is featured.

1 Look at some of the **key themes** in *Macbeth* below. Complete ✏ these notes with **a key plot event** in which each theme is relevant.

power	
ambition	
good and evil	*Lady Macbeth calls upon the forces of evil to 'fill' her with 'direst cruelty'.*
violence	
the supernatural	
guilt	*Macbeth is filled with guilt after killing King Duncan.*
loyalty	

2 A **key theme** is an idea that Shakespeare explores in different ways at different points in the play. Look at some of the key scenes in which Shakespeare explores the theme of **power**.

- Duncan rewards his loyal Thanes while Macbeth plots to kill him and take his power.

- When he acts on their predictions, Shakespeare shows the witches' power over Macbeth.

- In persuading Macbeth to kill Duncan, Lady Macbeth shows her power over him.

- Macbeth murders Duncan in order to gain power.

- Macbeth has those who threaten his power murdered: Banquo and Macduff's family.

a How does Shakespeare present power in the play? Circle Ⓐ any of the ideas below.

positive		*neutral*		*negative*	
exciting	*rewarding*	*necessary*	*a great responsibility*	*corrupting*	*dangerous*

b Write ✏ **one** or **two** sentences explaining your ideas.

....

....

....

3 How do I comment on the development of character or theme?

One way to explore how characters develop is to **compare** how they are presented at the start and end of the play; one way to explore how themes develop is to **compare** how they are presented in different key scenes in the play.

(1) Look at these key moments in the development of the character of Lady Macbeth.

- When she first appears in the play, in Act 1 Scene 5, ...
  ....

- In Act 1 Scene 7, she persuades her husband to overcome his fears and kill King Duncan.
- In Act 2 Scene 2, she assures Macbeth that 'a little water clears us of this deed'.
- In Act 3 Scene 2, she admits to herself that she is anxious about the murder of Duncan.
- In her final appearance in the play, in Act 5 Scene 1, ...
  ....

- Near the end of the play, we are told that ....
  ....

   (a) Complete ✏ the notes above, summing up how Lady Macbeth is presented at the start and end of the play.

   (b) How does Lady Macbeth's character develop during the course of the play? Write ✏ **two** or **three** sentences summing up your ideas.

....

....

....

(2) Look at these four key moments in the play at which the theme of violence is shown.

- In Act 1 Scene 2, we hear about Macbeth's victory in battle, when he 'unseam'd' Macdonwald 'from the nave to th' chops, / And fix'd his head upon our battlements'.

- In Act 2 Scene 2, Macbeth murders King Duncan.

- In Act 4 Scene 2, Macbeth has Macduff's wife and children 'savagely slaughtered'.

- At the end of the play, Macbeth is killed. His severed head is carried on stage.

   (a) Think about how violence is presented in the play. Tick ✓ any of the statements below that you agree with.

A	Violence is always wrong.	☐	C Violence always leads to more violence.	☐
B	Violence is sometimes necessary and acceptable.	☐	D Violence always has negative consequences.	☐

   (b) Write ✏ **one** or **two** sentences on paper summing up your thoughts about the presentation of violence in *Macbeth*.

Unit 4 Exploring themes and characters   **29**

Exploring themes and characters

To explore the themes and characters in Macbeth effectively, you need to:

- identify significant key events in the play in which those characters or themes are shown
- compare how they are presented in those key events.

Look at this exam-style question you saw at the start of the unit.

Exam-style question

Starting with this extract, explore how Shakespeare presents good and evil in the play.

Write about:

- how Shakespeare presents Macbeth and Lady Macbeth as good or evil in this extract
- how Shakespeare presents good and evil in the play as a whole.

(1) Now look at these two paragraphs, written by a student in response to the exam-style question above.

One way in which Shakespeare clearly presents evil is in the character of Macbeth almost from the beginning of the play. While Duncan is praising and rewarding Macbeth for winning the battle against the Norwegians, Macbeth is expressing his 'deep and dark desires' to fulfil the witches' predictions and take the throne from Duncan's family. This shows him as deceitful and ungrateful and ruthless in his ambition for power. It is his selfishness and cold-blooded planning that make him seem so evil.

This also contrasts with Banquo. Macbeth and Banquo are friends at the start of the play; they are both given predictions by the witches, and they are both praised and promised rewards by King Duncan. However, Banquo remains loyal to the king. Later in the play, an increasingly evil Macbeth has the good Banquo murdered, perhaps suggesting that evil is stronger than good, or perhaps that evil is very dangerous and that good must challenge and overcome it, which Banquo does not do, even though he suspects Macbeth has 'played most foully.'

a Circle (A) and label (✏) **all** the key scenes or events in the play that this student has referred to in these paragraphs.

b Underline (A) and label (✏) where in these paragraphs this student **comments** on how Shakespeare presents good and evil in these key scenes or events.

c Highlight (✏) and label (✏) where in these paragraphs this student **compares** key scenes or events in which good and evil are presented in the play as a whole to develop her ideas.

Your turn!

You are now going to **write two paragraphs** in response to the exam-style question.

Exam-style question

Starting with this extract, explore how Shakespeare presents good and evil in the play.

Write about:

• how Shakespeare presents Macbeth and Lady Macbeth as good or evil in this extract

• how Shakespeare presents good and evil in the play as a whole.

(30 marks)

AO4 (4 marks)

(1) Which key scenes or events in the play could you focus on in your response? Note ✎ **four** of your ideas below.

Think about:

(?) Which characters in the play are shown as good or evil? Which key scenes or events show this most clearly?

(?) Are these characters completely good? Are they thoroughly evil? Or are there other key scenes or events in the play which show them in a different light?

1

2

3

4

(2) Look carefully at the key scenes or events you have chosen. What do they suggest about how good and/or evil are presented in the play? Add ✎ to your notes.

(3) Now compare how good and evil are presented in the different key scenes or events you have noted above. What does your comparison suggest about the way in which good or evil are presented in the play? Add ✎ to your notes.

(4) Write ✎ your paragraphs in response to the exam-style question above on paper.

Review your skills

Check up

Review your response to the exam-style question on page 31. Tick ✓ the column to show how well you think you have done each of the following.

	Not quite ✓	Nearly there ✓	Got it! ✓
identified significant scenes or events in the play showing the theme of good and/or evil	☐	☐	☐
commented on how good and/or evil are presented in each significant scene or event	☐	☐	☐
developed my ideas by comparing how good and/or evil are presented in key scenes or events	☐	☐	☐

Need more practice?

Here is another exam-style question, this time relating to the extract from Act 3 Scene 1 on page 74 (Extract B).

Exam-style question

Starting with this extract, explain how far you think Shakespeare explores the consequences of dishonesty and deception in *Macbeth*.

Write about:

- how Shakespeare presents Banquo and Macbeth as dishonest and deceitful in this extract
- how Shakespeare presents the consequences of dishonesty and deception in the play as a whole.

(30 marks)

AO4 (4 marks)

Write ✏ **two** paragraphs in response to this question, focusing on the second bullet point: **the play as a whole.**

You'll find some suggested ideas in the Answers section.

How confident do you feel about each of these **skills?** Colour ✏ in the bars.

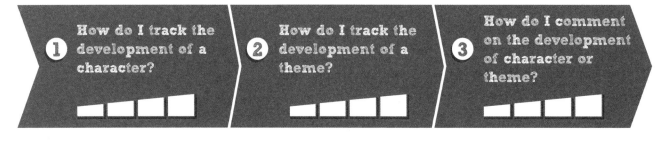

1 How do I track the development of a character?

2 How do I track the development of a theme?

3 How do I comment on the development of character or theme?

(5) Planning your response

This unit will help you to plan your response to the exam question. The skills you will build are to:

- develop a critical judgement in response to the focus of the exam question
- support your judgement with relevant points
- sequence your points to build a successful argument in support of your judgement.

In the exam you will face a question like the one below. This is about the extract on the next page. At the end of the unit you will **write your own response** to this question.

Exam-style question

Starting with this extract, write about how Shakespeare explores guilt in *Macbeth*.

Write about:

- how Shakespeare presents guilt in this extract
- how Shakespeare explores guilt in the play as a whole.

(30 marks)

AO4 (4 marks)

Before you tackle the question you will work through three key questions in the **skills boosts** to help you plan your response.

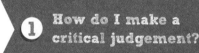

1 How do I make a critical judgement? > **2 How do I gather relevant points?** > **3 How do I sequence my points?**

Read the extract on the next page from Act 2 Scene 2 of *Macbeth*.

As you read, think about the following:

What has happened before this scene? What happens after this scene? ☐	How does Shakespeare present Macbeth's thoughts and feelings in this extract? ☐	How does Shakespeare present Lady Macbeth's thoughts and feelings in this extract? ☐

Exam-style question

Read the following extract from Act 2 Scene 2 of *Macbeth*.

At this point in the play, Macbeth has just murdered Duncan and still has Duncan's blood on his hands. He has heard the voices of Duncan's two sons as he returned to his wife.

Extract A | Act 2 Scene 2 of *Macbeth*

MACBETH
This is a sorry sight.
Looking on his hands
LADY MACBETH
A foolish thought, to say a sorry sight.
MACBETH
There's one did laugh in's sleep, and one cried 'Murder!'
5   That they did wake each other: I stood and heard them:
But they did say their prayers, and address'd them
Again to sleep.
LADY MACBETH
There are two lodged together.
MACBETH
One cried 'God bless us!' and 'Amen' the other;
10   As they had seen me with these hangman's hands.
Listening their fear, I could not say 'Amen,'
When they did say 'God bless us!'
LADY MACBETH
Consider it not so deeply.
MACBETH
But wherefore could not I pronounce 'Amen'?
15   I had most need of blessing, and 'Amen'
Stuck in my throat.
LADY MACBETH
These deeds must not be thought
After these ways; so, it will make us mad.
MACBETH
Methought I heard a voice cry 'Sleep no more!
20   Macbeth does murder sleep', the innocent sleep,
Sleep that knits up the ravell'd sleeve of care,
The death of each day's life, sore labour's bath,
Chief nourisher in life's feast,--
LADY MACBETH
What do you mean?
MACBETH
25   Still it cried 'Sleep no more!' to all the house:
'Glamis hath murder'd sleep, and therefore Cawdor
Shall sleep no more; Macbeth shall sleep no more.'

How do I make a critical judgement?

Before you plan your written response, you need to make a **critical judgement** on the topic in the question. This means weighing up the key evidence in the play and coming to a conclusion: a sentence or two that sums up your ideas.

① One way to begin developing your critical judgement is to focus on the extract you are given in the question. Look at two quotations from Extract A on page 34.

Lady Macbeth   **Macbeth**

> These deeds must not be thought
> After these ways; so, it will make us mad.

> Still it cried 'Sleep no more!' to all the house:
> 'Glamis hath murder'd sleep, and therefore Cawdor
> Shall sleep no more; Macbeth shall sleep no more.'

ⓐ How do Macbeth and Lady Macbeth react to the murder of King Duncan?
   Note 🖉 your ideas in the boxes above. Think about:

   • how each character expresses (or does not express) any feelings of guilt

   • the impact that guilt can have.

ⓑ Write 🖉 **one** or **two** sentences summing up your **critical judgement** on how guilt is presented **in the extract**.

....

....

② Now you need to think about how guilt is explored **in the play as a whole**. Look at these other scenes which show characters affected by guilt.

| 3.2 | Lady Macbeth admits to herself that she is anxious about the murder of Duncan. Macbeth tells her that his mind is 'full of scorpions'. | | 3.4 | Macbeth sees Banquo's ghost. | | 5.1 | Lady Macbeth sleepwalks: 'will these hands ne'er be clean?' | |

ⓐ Which of these scenes could be used as evidence to **support** or **develop** the critical judgement that you made in ① ⓑ? Tick ✓ them.

ⓑ Which of these scenes **contradict** the critical judgement that you made? Cross ✗ them.

ⓒ Is your critical judgement on how Shakespeare explores guilt in *Macbeth* still valid? Or do you need to rethink it now that you have considered some of the other scenes in which guilt is shown? Either tick ✓ your answer to ① ⓑ, or rewrite 🖉 it below.

....

....

2 How do I gather relevant points?

You need to gather a range of points from the extract and from the whole play to support and develop the critical judgement you make in response to the exam question.

(1) Think about how guilt is presented **in the extract** on page 34 and **in the whole play**.

    a   Look at some different critical judgements about the presentation of guilt in *Macbeth* below. For each one, circle (A) the number on the scale to show how strongly you agree or disagree.

	Disagree	Unsure	Agree
A Feelings of guilt can be very destructive.	1	2	3
B Feelings of guilt can be overcome or ignored.	1	2	3
C The audience expects characters that do wrong to feel guilt.	1	2	3
D The audience symathises with characters who feel guilt.	1	2	3
E The audience wants characters who do wrong to be punished – regardless of whether they feel guilt.	1	2	3

    b   Now look at some of the key scenes from the play below. Select key scenes that support each of the judgements that you agreed with, labelling (✎) them **A, B, C**, etc. to show which judgement they support.

| 2.2 | Macbeth is filled with guilt. Lady Macbeth assures Macbeth that 'a little water clears us of this deed'. |

| 3.2 | Lady Macbeth admits to herself that she is anxious about the murder of Duncan. Macbeth tells her that his mind is 'full of scorpions'. |

| 3.4 | Macbeth sees Banquo's ghost. |

| 4.2 | Macbeth has Macduff's family murdered. He expresses no guilt following this scene. |

| 5.1 | Lady Macbeth sleepwalks: 'will these hands ne'er be clean?' |

| 5.8 | Macbeth is killed. |

(2)   a   Review all of your answers on this page so far. Use them to note (✎) down in the table **three** key points you might make in your response to the exam-style question.

    b   For each key point, note (✎) the key scenes from the play that you could refer to as **evidence** to support your point.

	Key point	Evidence
1		
2		
3		

3 How do I sequence my points?

You need to sequence your key points to build a logical argument that supports your critical judgement. You need to start with the extract – but where do you go from there?

Look at this exam-style question, and one student's critical judgement in response to it.

Exam-style question

Starting with this extract, write about how Shakespeare explores guilt in *Macbeth*.

Macbeth and Lady Macbeth's feelings of guilt change dramatically during the play but in different ways. She is destroyed by guilt. His lack of guilt leads to his death.

Now look at these four key points, taken from the same student's plan.

A
Macbeth filled with guilt at murder of Duncan.

B
Lady Macbeth driven mad by guilt.

C
Macbeth's guilt disappears as he has Banquo and Macduff's family murdered.

D
Lady Macbeth shows no guilt at murder of Duncan.

1 One way to sequence the key points in a response is to work your way through the play **chronologically**: exploring how a character or theme develops as the play progresses.

How would you sequence the four key points above if you were organising this response **chronologically**? Write ✏️ the letters A–D in the order in which you would sequence them.

☐ ☐ ☐ ☐

2 Another way to organise the key points in a response is to **synthesise** your key points: grouping related points together.

For example, you could:

a group your key points by **character**. ☐

How would you sequence the key points above if you were going to explore how Shakespeare shows guilt first in one **character** and then another? Write ✏️ the letters A–D.

☐ ☐ ☐ ☐

Or you could:

b group your key points by **approach**. ☐

How would you sequence the key points above if you were going to look at one way in which Shakespeare explores guilt, and then another way in which Shakespeare explores guilt? ✏️

☐ ☐ ☐ ☐

3 Look at all of your answers above. Which method would **you** choose to sequence the key points above? Tick ✓ it.

Planning your response

To plan an effective response, you need to:

- make a critical judgement summing up your response to the focus of the question
- gather relevant points: identify the key moments in the play that support your critical judgement and use them to develop points you can make in your response
- sequence your points: decide on the most effective way to build a logical argument that supports your critical judgement: for example, chronologically, or by character, or by approach.

Look at this exam-style question you saw at the start of the unit.

Exam-style question

Starting with this extract, write about how Shakespeare explores guilt in *Macbeth*.

Write about:

- how Shakespeare presents guilt in this extract
- how Shakespeare explores guilt in the play as a whole.

(1) Now look at these two paragraphs, written by a student in response to the exam-style question above.

> *Following the feelings of fear and guilt that Macbeth experienced after the murder of Duncan, Macbeth uses murderers to kill Banquo. This suggests that he is trying to distance himself from those feelings. However, Shakespeare develops Macbeth's guilt, showing it in the form of Banquo's ghost. This suggests that Macbeth is literally being haunted by his feelings of guilt and is terrified of them. It is this guilt that helps the audience to have some sympathy for Macbeth as it shows that he is not completely evil.*
>
> *However, in the second half of the play, Macbeth shows little guilt or remorse. He has Macduff's wife and children killed but, after he has ordered it to be done, does not mention it again. It seems that Macbeth is 'in blood stepped in so far' and so worried and obsessed with his life and his power falling apart, that he has lost his own feelings of guilt, suggesting that by the end of the play Shakespeare wants the audience to see him as either mad or evil.*

a Which of these critical judgements do these paragraphs support? Tick ✓ **one**, or more.

A Shakespeare explores guilt to show the destructive impact that the desire for power can have. ☐

B Shakespeare uses the characters' guilt to manipulate the audience's response to them. ☐

C Shakespeare shows that guilt can lead to madness. ☐

b How has this student organised their key points? Tick ✓ **one**.

A chronologically ☐

B by character ☐

C by approach ☐

Your turn!

You are now going to **write your own answer** in response to the exam-style question.

Exam-style question

Starting with this extract, write about how Shakespeare explores guilt in Macbeth.

Write about:

- how Shakespeare presents guilt in this extract
- how Shakespeare explores guilt in the play as a whole.

(30 marks)

AO4 (4 marks)

(1) Sum up 🖉 your **critical judgement** in response to the exam-style question above. This will be the **conclusion** that your response must support.

....

....

....

(2) Which **key events or scenes** in the play will you explore in your response to support your critical judgement? Note 🖉 them below.

(3) Note 🖉 down all the **key points** you will make about these key events or scenes to support your critical judgement.

....

....

....

....

(4) **a** How will you sequence your key points? Tick ✓ **one** answer.

chronologically ▢   by character ▢   by approach ▢

b Number 🖉 your key points in (3), sequencing them to build an argument that supports your critical judgement.

(5) Now write 🖉 your response to the exam-style question above on paper.

Review your skills

Check up

Review your response to the exam-style question on page 39. Tick ✓ the column to show how well you think you have done each of the following.

	Not quite ✓	Nearly there ✓	Got it! ✓
made a critical judgement	☐	☐	☐
made key points using key scenes and events in the play to support my critical judgement	☐	☐	☐
sequenced my key points to build an argument that supports my critical judgement	☐	☐	☐

Look over all of your work in this unit. Note 🖉 down the **three** most important things to remember when planning your response.

1. ....

2. ....

3. ....

Need more practice?

Here is another exam-style question, this time relating to Act 3 Scene 2 on page 75 (Extract C).

Exam-style question

Starting with this extract, explore how Shakespeare presents false appearances in *Macbeth*.

Write about:

- the false appearances that Macbeth and Lady Macbeth show and talk about in this extract
- how Shakespeare presents false appearances in the play as a whole. (30 marks)

AO4 (4 marks)

Plan 🖉 your response to this question. Aim to:

- sum up your critical judgement in one or two sentences
- identify key events to focus on, and key points to make
- sequence your ideas.

You'll find some suggested ideas in the Answers section.

How confident do you feel about each of these skills? Colour 🖉 in the bars.

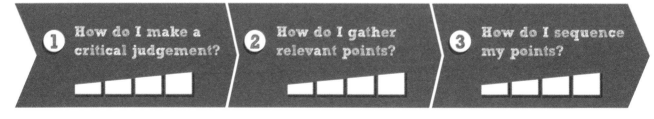

1 How do I make a critical judgement?

2 How do I gather relevant points?

3 How do I sequence my points?

Get started

Read, understand and respond to texts (AO1); Analyse the language, form and structure used by a writer to create meanings and effects (AO2)

 Writing your response

This unit will help you write the part of your response in which you have to focus on **the play as a whole**. The skills you will build are to:

- know key events and key quotations you can use when writing about the play as a whole
- understand how to use key events and quotations as evidence
- be able to analyse evidence from the play effectively.

In the exam you will face a question like the one below. This is about the extract on the next page. At the end of the unit you will **write your own response** to the **second part** of this question.

Reminder: For more help on writing about **the extract**, see Units 2 and 3.

Exam-style question

Starting with this extract, explain how far you think Shakespeare shows Macbeth in control of events in the play.

Write about:

- how Shakespeare presents Macbeth at this moment in the play
- how Shakespeare presents Macbeth in the play as a whole.

(30 marks)

AO4 (4 marks)

Before you tackle the question you will work through three key questions in the **skills boosts** to help you write your response.

1 How do I choose key events and key quotations to learn?

2 How do I use evidence to support my ideas?

3 How do I analyse my evidence?

Read the extract on the next page from *Act 3 Scene 4* of *Macbeth*.

As you read, think about the following:

What has happened before this scene? What happens after this scene?

How does Shakespeare present Macbeth's thoughts and feelings in this extract?

How does Shakespeare present Lady Macbeth's thoughts and feelings in this extract?

Exam-style question

Read the following extract from Act 3 Scene 4 of *Macbeth*.

At this point in the play, Macbeth and Lady Macbeth are holding a banquet to celebrate Macbeth becoming the King of Scotland. The ghost of Banquo has appeared and is sitting in Macbeth's place.

Extract A | Act 3 Scene 4 of *Macbeth*

ROSS
Please't your Highness
To grace us with your royal company.
MACBETH
The table's full.
LENNOX
Here is a place reserved, sir.
MACBETH
5   Where?
LENNOX
Here, my good lord. What is't that moves your Highness?
MACBETH
Which of you have done this?
Lords
What, my good lord?
MACBETH
Thou canst not say I did it: never shake
10   Thy gory locks at me.
ROSS
Gentlemen, rise: his Highness is not well.
LADY MACBETH
Sit, worthy friends: my lord is often thus,
And hath been from his youth: pray you, keep seat;
The fit is momentary; upon a thought
15   He will again be well: if much you note him,
You shall offend him and extend his passion:
Feed, and regard him not. Are you a man?
MACBETH
Ay, and a bold one, that dare look on that
Which might appal the devil.
LADY MACBETH
20   O proper stuff!
This is the very painting of your fear:
This is the air-drawn dagger which, you said,
Led you to Duncan. O, these flaws and starts,
Impostors to true fear, would well become
25   A woman's story at a winter's fire,
Authorized by her grandam. Shame itself!
Why do you make such faces? When all's done,
You look but on a stool.

1 How do I choose key events and key quotations to learn?

When you write about the **extract**, you should support your response with quotations from the extract. When you write about the **play as a whole**, you should refer to key events and scenes. You can also use some key quotations that you have learned to show your detailed understanding of the play.

Reminder: For more help on writing about the **extract**, see Units 2 and 3.

The key events in the play are those which: show a significant aspect of a key character **or** explore a key theme **or** are significant to the plot – the play would not develop in the same way without them.

1 Look at the extract from Act 3 Scene 4 on page 42 (Extract A). **Add** ✎ or **delete** ~~cat~~ words from the sentences below to explain the significance of this moment in the play.

a *This moment in the play reveals something about Macbeth and Lady Macbeth.*

b *The themes of the supernatural, guilt, power and deception are all relevant to this moment.*

2 Now look at some of the other events in Act 3, the middle of the play.

| 3.1 | Banquo suspects Macbeth has 'play'd most foully'. He is going out riding. Macbeth persuades two murderers to kill Banquo and his son, Fleance. |

| 3.2 | Lady Macbeth is anxious about the murder of Duncan. Macbeth is anxious that Banquo is still alive. |

| 3.3 | Banquo is murdered. Fleance escapes. |

| 3.5 | The witches know Macbeth will visit them again. |

| 3.6 | Lennox and a Lord discuss the deaths of Banquo and Duncan. |

a Which scenes reveal something about key characters? Highlight ✎ those characters' names.

b Which are significant to the plot? Label ✎ them '**plot**'.

c Review your answers to questions 1 and 2. Which key scenes and events in Act 3 should you make sure you know? Tick ✓ them.

3 The best quotations to learn are short, and can be used to support two (or more) different ideas. Look at some of Lady Macbeth's lines.

A unsex me here,
And fill me from the crown to the toe top-full
Of direst cruelty! (1.5)

B I would, while it was smiling in my face,
Have pluck'd my nipple from his boneless gums,
And dash'd the brains out (1.7)

C look like the innocent flower,
But be the serpent under't (1.5)

D A little water clears us of this deed (2.2)

a Which quotation most effectively shows Lady Macbeth's ruthless ambition? Tick ✓ at least one.

b Which also reveal something about her relationship with Macbeth? Circle Ⓐ at least one.

c Which quotation will you learn off by heart to support the point that Lady Macbeth is ruthless and to show her relationship with Macbeth? Highlight ✎ it.

d Look at the quotation you have chosen. How could you make it shorter? Underline Ⓐ the most significant or revealing phrase of two to four words.

② How do I use evidence to support my ideas?

You can use **key events** in the play and **key quotations** as evidence to **support** and **explain** your ideas.

Look at one student's **key idea**, or **critical judgement**, in response to this exam question.

Exam-style question

Starting with this extract, explain how far you think Shakespeare shows Macbeth in control of events in the play.

Macbeth is not at all in control of events in the play.

① Look again at Extract A on page 42. Note ✎ down **one key event** and **one key quotation** from this point in the play to support the student's **key idea**.

Key event: ....

Key quotation: ....

② Now think about **key events** elsewhere in the play. Which would support the key idea above?

Note ✎ down **two** key events.

Hint: Think about:
• what Macbeth **does** in the play
• things that **happen to** Macbeth.

1 ....

2 ....

③ Which **key quotations** from the play would support the key idea above? Tick ✓ **one or more** of these **key Macbeth quotes**, or note ✎ your own on paper.

A | **1.2** | Captain reporting on battle | ☐

brave Macbeth – well he deserves that name

B | **1.4** | plots to become king | ☐

Stars, hide your fires;
Let not light see my black and deep desires

C | **1.5** | Lady Macbeth thinks he is | ☐

too full o' the milk of human kindness

D | **2.2** | guilt about murder of Duncan | ☐

Macbeth shall sleep no more

E | **3.2** | sees Banquo as a threat | ☐

O, full of scorpions is my mind, dear wife!

F | **3.4** | no turning back now! | ☐

I am in blood Stepped in so far that, should I wade no more, Returning were as tedious as go o'er.

G | **5.5** | Losing hope | ☐

Tomorrow and tomorrow and tomorrow
Creeps in this petty pace from day to day

H | **5.8** | Believes he is invincible | ☐

I bear a charmed life

④ Review the evidence you have gathered above. Which supports the key idea at the top of this page more effectively? ✓

☐ The key events you noted in ②? ☐ The quotations you selected in ③? ☐ or both?

③ How do I analyse my evidence?

Every key **idea or point** you make should be supported with **evidence** which you can **analyse**, exploring the effect of the writer's choices of language and structure, what it suggests about theme and character, and its impact on the audience.

Look at one student's key idea, or **critical judgement**, on the theme of control in Macbeth.

At some points in the play, Macbeth believes he is in control.

Now look at a **key quotation** you could use as evidence to support this key idea.

At the end of the play, Macbeth tells Macduff 'I bear a (charmed) life'.

To develop an effective analysis, think about these **five areas** of analysis:

A **Explain the quote in the context of the play:** Why does Macbeth think this?

He believes the witches' predictions – he cannot be killed by Macduff and thinks it gives him control of the situation. ☐

B **Think about language and structure:** What does the word 'charmed' suggest?

'charmed' suggests he is protected by magic – he has special, supernatural power. ☐

C **Think about character:** What does this suggest about Macbeth's character?

He is strongly influenced by the supernatural – it controls his actions and choices. ☐

D **Think about theme:** What does this suggest about the theme of control?

Events are not in his control because he believes the supernatural will save him. ☐

E **Think about Shakespeare's intention:** How does Shakespeare want the audience to respond to Macbeth at this point in the play?

A tense, exciting moment: will the supernatural protect Macbeth or will Macduff end Macbeth's tyranny? ☐

① Look at one student's ideas for analysis of the **key quotation** above. Which ideas would you include in your analysis of this quote? Tick ⊘ them.

② Now look at a key event that you could use as evidence to support the key idea above.

In Act 4, Macbeth has Macduff's family murdered.

Use the **five areas of analysis** above to help you note ✐ some ideas you could use in your analysis of this key event.

Writing your response

To write an effective response, you should:

- be familiar with the key events of the play
- know some key quotations from the play off by heart
- use key events and key quotations as evidence to support your ideas about the play's key themes and characters
- analyse your evidence, thinking about language, structure, theme, character and Shakespeare's intention.

Look at this exam-style question you saw on page 41.

Exam-style question

Starting with this extract, explain how far you think Shakespeare shows Macbeth in control of events in the play.

Write about:

- how Shakespeare presents Macbeth at this moment in the play
- how Shakespeare presents Macbeth in the play as a whole.

Now look at a paragraph focusing on the play as a whole, taken from one student's response to the question.

At the beginning of the play, Macbeth appears to be in control of his destiny. He hears the witches' prediction that he will be King of Scotland and almost immediately begins to think about how he will make this prediction come true. He talks about his 'black and deep desires' as he watches Duncan announce that Malcolm will be the next king. Describing his ambitions as 'deep' suggests how strongly he feels them, and the word 'black' suggests that he knows they are wrong. At this point Shakespeare is creating a sense of excitement for the audience, presenting Macbeth as a villain threatening to take control of the situation. However, it is not long before Macbeth becomes less sure of his 'desires' and is forced to let Lady Macbeth take control.

uses a key event as evidence

uses a quotation as evidence

explains the context of the evidence

analysis comments on the writer's choices of language and/or structure

analysis comments on character

analysis comments on theme

analysis comments on Shakespeare's intention

(1) Can you identify all the different things the student has included in this paragraph?
Link ✐ the annotations to the paragraph to show where the student has included them.

Your turn!

You are now going to **write your own answer** in response to the exam-style question.

Exam-style question

Starting with this extract, explain how far you think Shakespeare shows Macbeth in control of events in the play.

Write about:

- how Shakespeare presents Macbeth at this moment in the play
- how Shakespeare presents Macbeth in the play as a whole.

(30 marks)

AO4 (4 marks)

(1) Write 🖉 **one** or **two** sentences summarising your critical judgement in response to the question: Is Macbeth in control?

....

....

(2) Which key events in the play would support your critical judgement? Note 🖉 them below.

(3) Which quotations could you explore in your response? Add 🖉 them above.

(4) Look at all the evidence you have gathered. Think about:
- language and structure in your quotations
- what your evidence suggests about Macbeth's character
- what your evidence suggests about the theme you are exploring: is Macbeth in control?
- what your evidence suggests about Shakespeare's intention: how might the audience respond at this point?

Annotate 🖉 your evidence with your ideas.

(5) Look at your annotated evidence.

a Which are your strongest ideas? Tick ✓ them.

b Number 🖉 the ideas that you have ticked, sequencing them to build an argument that supports your critical judgement.

(6) Now write 🖉 your response to the exam-style question above on paper.

Review your skills

Check up

Review your response to the exam-style question on page 47. Tick ✓ the column to show how well you think you have done each of the following.

	Not quite ✓	Nearly there ✓	Got it! ✓
selected relevant key events to support my critical judgement	☐	☐	☐
selected relevant key quotations to support my critical judgement	☐	☐	☐
analysed my evidence effectively	☐	☐	☐

Look over all of your work in this unit. Note ✐ down the **three** most important things to remember when writing your response.

1. ....

2. ....

3. ....

Need more practice?

Here is another exam-style question, this time relating to Act 3 Scene 2 of *Macbeth* on page 75 (Extract C).

Exam-style question

Starting with this extract, explore how Shakespeare presents falase appearances in *Macbeth*.

Write about:

* the false appearances that Macbeth and Lady Macbeth show and talk about in this extract
* how Shakespeare presents false appearances in the play as a whole.

(30 marks)

AO4 (4 marks)

Write ✐ your response to this question.

You'll find some suggested points to refer to in the Answers section.

How confident do you feel about each of these **skills**? Colour ✐ in the bars.

1 How do I choose key events and key quotations to learn?

2 How do I use evidence to support my ideas?

3 How do I analyse my evidence?

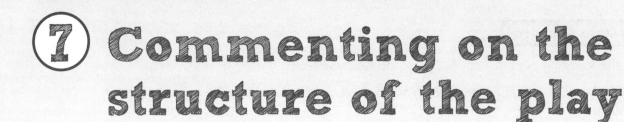

⑦ Commenting on the structure of the play

This unit will help you to comment on Shakespeare's structural choices in *Macbeth*. The skills you will build are to:

- identify significant structural features of the play
- explore the impact of some of the structural features of the play
- build comments on the play's structure into your analysis.

In the exam you will face a question like the one below. This is about the extract on the next page. At the end of the unit you will **write your own response** to this question.

Exam-style question

Starting with this extract, explore how Shakespeare presents the power of predictions in *Macbeth*.

Write about:

- how Shakespeare presents the power of predictions at this moment in the play
- how Shakespeare presents the power of predictions in the play as a whole.

(30 marks)

AO4 (4 marks)

Before you tackle the question you will work through three key questions in the **skills boosts** to help you comment on the structure of the play.

 1 **How can I comment on the structure of the play?**

 2 **How do I comment on the impact of structure?**

 3 **How do I analyse the writer's use of structure?**

Read the extract on the next page from Act 4 Scene 1 of *Macbeth*.

As you read, think about the following:

What has happened before this scene? What happens after this scene?	How does Shakespeare present the witches in this extract?	How does Shakespeare present Macbeth's thoughts and feelings in this extract?
⬚	⬚	⬚

Read the following extract from Act 4 Scene 1 of *Macbeth*.

At this point in the play, Macbeth hears three predictions made by three apparitions conjured by the witches.

Extract A | Act 4 Scene 1 of *Macbeth*

Thunder. First Apparition: an armed Head
MACBETH
Tell me, thou unknown power,--
First Witch
He knows thy thought:
Hear his speech, but say thou nought.
First Apparition
Macbeth! Macbeth! Macbeth! beware Macduff;
5   Beware the Thane of Fife. Dismiss me. Enough.

Descends

MACBETH
Whate'er thou art, for thy good caution, thanks;
Thou hast harp'd my fear aright: but one word more,--
First Witch
He will not be commanded: here's another,
More potent than the first.

Thunder. Second Apparition: A bloody Child

Second Apparition
10 Macbeth! Macbeth! Macbeth!
MACBETH
Had I three ears, I'd hear thee.
Second Apparition
Be bloody, bold, and resolute; laugh to scorn
The power of man, for none of woman born
Shall harm Macbeth.

Descends

MACBETH
15 Then live, Macduff: what need I fear of thee?
But yet I'll make assurance double sure,
And take a bond of fate: thou shalt not live;
That I may tell pale-hearted fear it lies,
And sleep in spite of thunder.

Thunder. Third Apparition: a Child crowned, with a tree in his hand

20 What is this
That rises like the issue of a king,
And wears upon his baby-brow the round
And top of sovereignty?
ALL
Listen, but speak not to't.
Third Apparition
25 Be lion-mettled, proud; and take no care
Who chafes, who frets, or where conspirers are:
Macbeth shall never vanquish'd be until
Great Birnam wood to high Dunsinane hill
Shall come against him.

Descends

MACBETH
30 That will never be.
Who can impress the forest, bid the tree
Unfix his earth-bound root? Sweet bodements! good!

1 How can I comment on the structure of the play?

Plays often follow the fortunes and misfortunes of the key characters as they succeed or fail in overcoming difficulties. Plays are often structured to manipulate the audience's responses to those characters and their story.

1 Think about how Shakespeare has structured the play to manipulate his audience. Add 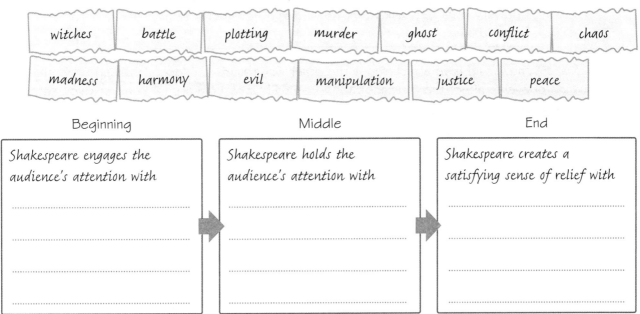 some or all of the words below, and/or some of your own ideas, to the flow chart beneath.

witches	battle	plotting	murder	ghost	conflict	chaos

madness	harmony	evil	manipulation	justice	peace

Beginning

Shakespeare engages the audience's attention with

....

....

....

Middle

Shakespeare holds the audience's attention with

....

....

....

End

Shakespeare creates a satisfying sense of relief with

....

....

....

2 Now think about how the key characters develop during the play.

a On the graph below, draw :

- a blue line tracking Macbeth's level of power over the course of the play. Label it 'M'.
- a blue line tracking Lady Macbeth's level of power over the course of the play. Label it 'LM'.
- a green line tracking how good or evil Macbeth seems at different stages of the play. Label it 'M'.
- a green line tracking how good or evil Lady Macbeth seems at different stages of the play. Label it 'LM'.

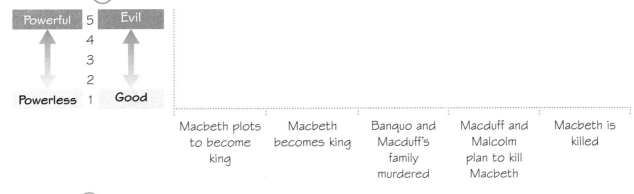

Powerful 5 Evil
         4
         3
         2
Powerless 1 Good

Macbeth plots to become king | Macbeth becomes king | Banquo and Macduff's family murdered | Macduff and Malcolm plan to kill Macbeth | Macbeth is killed

b Write one or two sentences describing your findings. How has Shakespeare used the development of key characters to structure the play?

....

....

② How do I comment on the impact of structure?

The sequence of key events in *Macbeth* has been structured to manipulate the audience's response to them. You can explore this when you write about the play.

① Think about the order of key events near the beginning of the play.

| 1.2 | The Captain reports Macbeth's bravery in battle; Duncan will reward him. | ➡ | 1.3 | Macbeth plots to become king. |

But Shakespeare could have structured it the other way round. How does Shakespeare's chosen sequence of events affect the audience's response to Macbeth? Write 🖉 **one** or **two** sentences explaining your ideas.

....

....

....

....

② Now think about the structure of the middle of the play.

| 3.3 | Macbeth has Banquo murdered. | ➡ | 4.2 | Macbeth has Macduff's family murdered. |

But Shakespeare could have structured it the other way round. Why might Shakespeare have chosen this sequence of events? Think about:

• who is being murdered and how the audience might respond to that

• how Macduff responds to the murder of his family.

Write 🖉 **one** or **two** sentences explaining your ideas.

....

....

....

....

③ Look again at Extract A on page 50. This is Macbeth's second encounter with the witches. Why might Shakespeare have decided not to combine these two encounters into one scene showing the witches giving Macbeth all their predictions at once? Write 🖉 **one** or **two** sentences explaining your ideas.

....

....

....

....

③ How do I analyse the writer's use of structure?

You can build effective comments on structure into your analysis of the play.

Look at some sentences taken from one student's response to an exam-style question.

Exam-style question

Explore how Shakespeare presents the power of predictions in *Macbeth*.

> The witches predict that Macbeth will be Thane of Cawdor and King of Scotland. When the first prediction comes true almost immediately, Macbeth begins plotting to make the second prediction come true. It is the witches' prediction that seems to plant the idea of murdering Duncan in Macbeth's mind.

① Now look at some sentences focusing on the play's structure that could be added to this paragraph.

A
> The witches appear on stage twice in the first three scenes of the play.

B
> The dramatic opening scene immediately engages the audience's interest and attention and is soon followed by a second dramatic appearance.

C
> This prediction is perhaps the most important single moment in the play as it sets off the sequence of events that the play follows to Macbeth's death.

D
> These predictions follow the news of Macbeth's bravery in battle, suggesting it is the witches that turn Macbeth from a brave and loyal subject into a traitor.

  ⓐ Which sentences would you add to the student's response paragraph above? Tick ✓ them.

  ⓑ Mark ✐ where you would add them by writing the letter **A**, **B**, **C**, etc. on the student's response paragraph above.

② Now look at another paragraph taken from the same student's response.

> Another consequence of the witches' predictions is the murder of Macduff's wife and children. The murder of Macduff's son is one of the few deaths that the audience sees take place on stage, making it even more shocking that Macbeth is responsible for the death of a child. This shows not only how ruthless and heartless Macbeth has become, but also the power and influence that the witches have over him.

  ⓐ Write ✐ **one** or **two** sentences that could be added to this paragraph, to develop the analysis by focusing on the play's structure.

....

....

....

  ⓑ Add ✐ an asterisk * to the student's response paragraph above to show where you would insert your sentence(s).

Commenting on the structure of the play

To comment on the structure of the play, you need to:

- identify significant structural choices that Shakespeare has made
- consider how Shakespeare has used these structural choices to manipulate the audience's response to the characters and events in the play
- link these structural features and their impact to the focus of the question.

Look at this exam-style question you saw at the start of the unit.

Exam-style question

Starting with this extract, explore how Shakespeare presents the power of predictions in *Macbeth*.

Write about:

- how Shakespeare presents the power of predictions at this moment in the play
- how Shakespeare presents the power of predictions in the play as a whole.

Now look at a paragraph taken from one student's response to the question.

> Macbeth's decision that most clearly shows the power of the witches' predictions, and their evil intentions, is the decision to slaughter Macduff's family, even though he knows that Macduff has fled to England. Shakespeare structures the play so that Macbeth follows the shocking killing of his friend Banquo with this even more disturbing mass murder. Banquo died but his innocent young son escaped, which Shakespeare might have intended to be a relief to the audience. Now, though, another child is not so lucky. Macduff's son is cruelly slaughtered on stage, shocking the audience by taking Macbeth's cruelty and violence a step further. It shows how low Macbeth has sunk and emphasises the power and evil influence of the witches' predictions.

1 What is the significant structural choice that the student explores in this paragraph? 🖉

....

....

....

2 Identify the part of the paragraph in which the student comments on how Shakespeare has used this structural choice to manipulate the audience's response. Underline Ⓐ it and label 🖉 it **'intention'**.

3 Identify the part of the paragraph in which the student links this structural feature and its impact to the focus of the question. Underline Ⓐ it and label 🖉 it **'question'**.

Your turn!

You are now going to **write your own answer** in response to the exam-style question.

Exam-style question

Starting with this extract, explore how Shakespeare presents the power of predictions in *Macbeth*.

Write about:

• how Shakespeare presents the power of predictions at this moment in the play

• how Shakespeare presents the power of predictions in the play as a whole.

(30 marks)

AO4 (4 marks)

1 Write ✐ **one** or **two** sentences summarising your critical judgement in response to the question.

....

....

2 Which key events and/or quotations would support your critical judgement? Note ✐ them below.

3 Look at all the evidence you have gathered. Think about how you could use it to comment on:

• **language and structure** in your quotations

• **character**

• the **theme** you are exploring: the power of predictions

• the **structure** of the play

• Shakespeare's **intention**: how might the audience respond?

Annotate ✐ your evidence with your ideas.

4 Look at your annotated evidence.

a Which are your strongest ideas? Tick ✓ them.

b Number ✐ the ideas that you have ticked and sequence them here to build an argument that supports your critical judgement.

5 Now write ✐ your response to the exam-style question above on paper.

Review your skills

Review your response to the exam-style question on page 55.

Check up

Review your response to the exam-style question on page 55. Tick ⊘ the column to show how well you think you have done each of the following.

	Not quite ⊘	Nearly there ⊘	Got it! ⊘
selected relevant evidence, commenting on character and theme	☐	☐	☐
identified relevant and significant structural features of the play	☐	☐	☐
commented on the impact of those structural features	☐	☐	☐
linked my comments on structure to the focus of the question	☐	☐	☐

Look over all of your work in this unit. Note ✐ down the **three** most important things to remember when commenting on the structure of the play.

1. ....
2. ....
3. ....

Need more practice?

Look at this exam-style question, this time relating to Act 4 Scene 3 of *Macbeth* on page 76 (Extract D).

Exam-style question

Starting with this extract, explore how Shakespeare presents violence and death in *Macbeth*. Write about:

- how Shakespeare presents the impact of violence and death at this moment in the play
- how Shakespeare presents violence and death in the play as a whole. (30 marks)

AO4 (4 marks)

Plan ✐ your response to the question.
- Which key events will you focus on? Note them down.
- Which key structural features of the play will you focus on? Add them to your plan.
- What impact do these structural features have on the presentation of violence and death in Macbeth? Note your ideas.

You'll find some suggested ideas in the Answers section.

How confident do you feel about each of these **skills?** Colour ✐ in the bars.

1 How can I comment on the structure of the play?

2 How do I comment on the impact of structure?

3 How do I analyse the writer's use of structure?

Show understanding of the relationships between texts and the contexts in which they were written (AO3)

(8) Commenting on context

This unit will help you to show your understanding of the play's context: its relationship with the time the play was written and first performed. The skills you will build are to:

- understand the relationship between the play and its context
- explain the impact of context on different elements of the play
- incorporate comments on context into your writing about the play.

In the exam you will face a question like the one below. This is about the extract on the next page. At the end of the unit you will **write your own response** to this question.

Exam-style question

Starting with this extract, explore how Shakespeare presents Lady Macbeth as a woman without a conscience.

Write about:

- how Shakespeare presents Lady Macbeth in this extract
- how Shakespeare presents Lady Macbeth in the play as a whole.

(30 marks)

AO4 (4 marks)

Before you tackle the question you will work through three key questions in the **skills boosts** to help you write about the play's context.

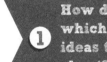 **1** How do I know which contextual ideas to write about? **2** How do I comment on context? **3** How do I build my comments on context into my analysis?

Read the extract on the next page from Act 5 Scene 1 of *Macbeth*.

As you read, think about the following: ⊘

What has happened before this scene? What happens after this scene?

How does Shakespeare present Lady Macbeth in this extract?

How does Shakespeare show her thoughts and feelings in this extract?

Exam-style question

Read the following extract from Act 5 Scene 1 of *Macbeth*.

At this point in the play, Lady Macbeth is sleepwalking, watched by her doctor and a gentlewoman.

Extract A | Act 5 Scene 1 of *Macbeth*

Doctor
What is it she does now? Look, how she rubs her hands.

Gentlewoman
It is an accustomed action with her, to seem thus
washing her hands: I have known her continue in
this a quarter of an hour.

LADY MACBETH
5   Yet here's a spot.

Doctor
Hark! she speaks: I will set down what comes from
her, to satisfy my remembrance the more strongly.

LADY MACBETH
Out, damned spot! out, I say!--One: two: why,
then, 'tis time to do't.--Hell is murky!--Fie, my
10   lord, fie! a soldier, and afeard? What need we
fear who knows it, when none can call our power to
account?--Yet who would have thought the old man
to have had so much blood in him.

Doctor
Do you mark that?

LADY MACBETH
15   The Thane of Fife had a wife: where is she now?--
What, will these hands ne'er be clean?--No more o'
that, my lord, no more o' that: you mar all with
this starting.

Doctor
Go to, go to; you have known what you should not.

Gentlewoman
20   She has spoke what she should not, I am sure of
that: heaven knows what she has known.

LADY MACBETH
Here's the smell of the blood still: all the
perfumes of Arabia will not sweeten this little
hand. Oh, oh, oh!

Doctor
25   What a sigh is there! The heart is sorely charged.

Gentlewoman
I would not have such a heart in my bosom for the
dignity of the whole body.

1 **How do I know which contextual ideas to write about?**

You need to be aware of all the different contexts of *Macbeth* on which you could comment so that you can choose those that are relevant to your response.

1 Look at some of the features of *Macbeth* and the time in which it was written. Tick ✓ any that are relevant to the play, and cross ✗ any that are not.

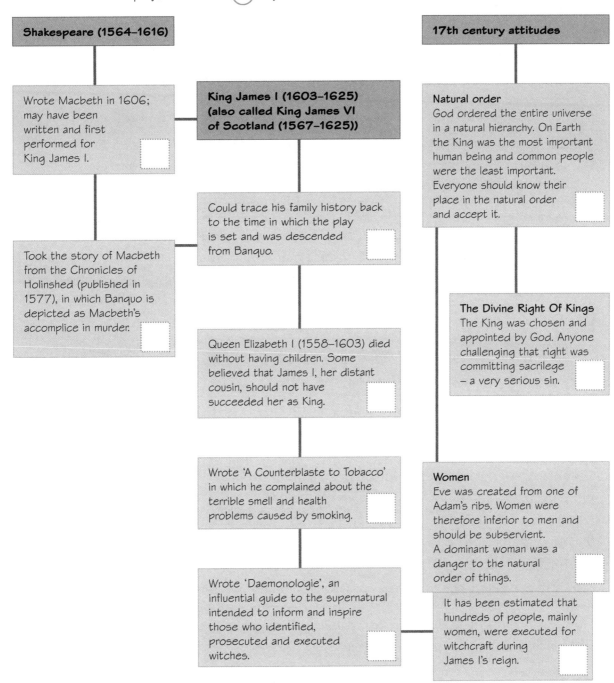

Shakespeare (1564–1616)

Wrote Macbeth in 1606; may have been written and first performed for King James I. ☐

Took the story of Macbeth from the Chronicles of Holinshed (published in 1577), in which Banquo is depicted as Macbeth's accomplice in murder. ☐

King James I (1603–1625) (also called King James VI of Scotland (1567–1625))

Could trace his family history back to the time in which the play is set and was descended from Banquo. ☐

Queen Elizabeth I (1558–1603) died without having children. Some believed that James I, her distant cousin, should not have succeeded her as King. ☐

Wrote 'A Counterblaste to Tobacco' in which he complained about the terrible smell and health problems caused by smoking. ☐

Wrote 'Daemonologie', an influential guide to the supernatural intended to inform and inspire those who identified, prosecuted and executed witches. ☐

17th century attitudes

Natural order
God ordered the entire universe in a natural hierarchy. On Earth the King was the most important human being and common people were the least important. Everyone should know their place in the natural order and accept it. ☐

The Divine Right Of Kings
The King was chosen and appointed by God. Anyone challenging that right was committing sacrilege – a very serious sin. ☐

Women
Eve was created from one of Adam's ribs. Women were therefore inferior to men and should be subservient.
A dominant woman was a danger to the natural order of things. ☐

It has been estimated that hundreds of people, mainly women, were executed for witchcraft during James I's reign. ☐

2 Now think about some of these key events and characters in the play.

| Macbeth | Lady Macbeth | The witches | Murder of Duncan |

Annotate 🖉 the diagram with these words, using arrows to link them to all the relevant elements of context.

2 How do I comment on context?

An effective comment on context can focus on **when** the play was written, and its impact on different audiences.

Look at the beginning of one student's paragraph exploring how Lady Macbeth is presented in Act 1 Scene 5.

> Lady Macbeth calls upon 'spirits' to fill her with 'direst cruelty', which suggests she is trying to use the power of witchcraft to achieve her ambitions.

1 Now look at some different students' comments on the context of the play in this scene.

A | Lady Macbeth is like a witch because people believed in them in those days.

B | Shakespeare uses his seventeenth-century audience's fear of witchcraft to make Lady Macbeth a terrifying character.

C | To a twenty-first-century audience, Lady Macbeth seems cruel, powerful and manipulative, but to a seventeenth-century audience she would be much more disturbing: a witch threatening the power of the men around her and the natural order of things.

a Which comment does what? Circle Ⓐ or cross out (A̶) each letter in the table below.

Context	Comment		
identifies the time in which the play was written	A	B	C
identifies a relevant belief, attitude or situation at that time	A	B	C
considers Shakespeare's intention	A	B	C
considers the impact on an audience	A	B	C
compares today's audience with Shakespeare's audience	A	B	C

b Which of the comments above would you use when writing about Lady Macbeth in Act 1 Scene 5? Tick ✓ **one or more**.

2 Look at these sentences from the beginning of another student's paragraph about the witches.

> The play begins with a very short scene featuring the witches. It does not help to tell the story of 'Macbeth' but is very dramatic and engaging.

a Write ✏ **one** or **two** sentences adding a contextual comment to the paragraph.

Think about: Why would this scene be so dramatic and engaging for Shakespeare's audience?

....

....

b Check your comment. Does it achieve all or most of the criteria listed in question **1** **a**? Adjust ✏ it as necessary.

3 How do I build my comments on context into my analysis?

You do not need to make contextual comments in every paragraph of your response, but you do need to make them relevant to your analysis of the play.

Look at the opening of a paragraph from a student's response, commenting on the presentation of Lady Macbeth in Act 1 Scene 7.

In Act 1 Scene 7, Lady Macbeth tries to persuade her husband to keep his promise to kill King Duncan. She tells him that she would have 'dash'd' her baby's brains out if she had promised to do so.

(1) Now look at some sentences you could add to this paragraph.

A This violent, graphic example shows how desperate she is to influence Macbeth and achieve her own ambitions.

B This hideous image shows her cruelty and cold-heartedness. She would do anything to get her own way.

C This disturbing image reveals her impatience with Macbeth's failure to make a decision and act like a man.

D In showing her strength, she is challenging Macbeth's manliness and highlighting his weakness.

a To Shakespeare's audience she would appear even more powerful and Macbeth would seem even weaker.

b This makes her sound like a witch because the witches talk about murder and cold-hearted cruelty so it makes her more frightening because Shakespeare's audience would have been frightened of witches.

c Shakespeare's audience were worried about challenges to power because of the Gunpowder Plot and other threats to King James I and so they would have been disturbed by Lady Macbeth's challenge to Macbeth's power.

d This challenge to her husband would have shocked a seventeenth-century audience who expected women to be obedient and respectful to their husbands.

a The sentences either comment on the **impact** of the evidence in the paragraph or comment on the play's **context**. Decide which heading ('Impact' or 'Context') to add ✏ above each of the columns of text.

b Which comments on context are relevant to which comments on impact? Draw ✏ lines linking them.

c Which of the sentences above would you include in a paragraph analysing how Shakespeare presents Lady Macbeth in Act 1 Scene 7 and in what order would you sequence them? Write ✏ the sentence order here.

☐ ☐ ☐ ☐ ☐ ☐ ☐ ☐

Commenting on context

To comment effectively on context, you need to:

- use a relevant contextual point to develop your analysis of a key point, supported by evidence
- explore what this contextual idea adds to your understanding of Shakespeare's intention and his audience's response.

Look at this exam-style question you saw at the start of the unit.

Exam-style question

Starting with this extract, explore how Shakespeare presents Lady Macbeth as a woman without a conscience.

Write about:

- how Shakespeare presents Lady Macbeth in this extract
- how Shakespeare presents Lady Macbeth in the play as a whole.

(**1**) Now look at a paragraph focusing on the play as a whole, taken from one student's response to the question.

When Lady Macbeth reads Macbeth's letter about the witches' predictions, she calls on the forces of evil to 'unsex' her and fill her with 'direst cruelty' so that she has the power to persuade her husband to murder Duncan. This is a disturbing moment in the play for a modern audience as it suggests she is trying to overcome her conscience so that she can persuade Macbeth to commit murder. However, because Shakespeare's audience firmly believed in 'spirits' and witches and the harm that they could do to normal human beings, this would be a terrifying moment for them. Shakespeare wants his audience to be both shocked and disturbed by Lady Macbeth and even more so because this is her first appearance in the play.

- uses a key event as evidence
- uses a quotation as evidence
- comments on the impact of the evidence
- identifies a relevant contextual point
- explores Shakespeare's intention in the light of this contextual point
- explores the audience's response in the light of this contextual point

Can you identify all the different things the student has included in this paragraph? Link the annotations to the paragraph to show where the student has included them.

Your turn!

You are now going to **write your own answer** in response to the exam-style question.

1. Write 🖉 **one** or **two** sentences, summarising your critical judgement in response to the question: Does Shakespeare present Lady Macbeth as a woman without a conscience?

   ....

   ....

2. Which key events in the play would support your critical judgement? Note 🖉 them below.

3. Look at all the evidence you have gathered. Think about:
   - what your evidence suggests about Lady Macbeth
   - what your evidence suggests about Shakespeare's intention: how might the audience respond at this point?

   Annotate 🖉 your evidence with your ideas.

4. Now think about the relevant contextual points you could make in your response. Annotate 🖉 your evidence with your ideas.

5. Look at your annotated evidence.

   a. Which are your strongest ideas? Tick ✓ them.

   b. Number 🖉 the ideas that you have ticked, and sequence them here to build an argument that supports your critical judgement.

6. Now write 🖉 your response to the exam-style question above on paper.

Review your skills

Check up

Review your response to the exam-style question on page 63. Tick ✓ the column to show how well you think you have done each of the following.

	Not quite ✓	Nearly there ✓	Got it! ✓
identified relevant contextual points	☐	☐	☐
used relevant contextual points to develop my analysis	☐	☐	☐
explored Shakespeare's intention and the audience's response in the light of the play's context	☐	☐	☐

Look over all of your work in this unit. Note ✎ down the **three** most important things to remember when commenting on context.

1. ....

2. ....

3. ....

Need more practice?

Look at this exam-style question, this time relating to Act 5 Scene 3 on page 77 (Extract E).

Exam-style question

Starting with this extract, explain how far you think Shakespeare presents Macbeth as a brave and heroic man.

Write about:

• how Shakespeare presents Macbeth in this extract

• how Shakespeare presents Macbeth in the play as a whole.

(30 marks)

AO4 (4 marks)

Write ✎ your response to this question.

You'll find some suggested points to refer to in the Answers section.

How confident do you feel about each of these **skills?** Colour ✎ in the bars.

1 How do I know which contextual ideas to write about?

2 How do I comment on context?

3 How do I build my comments on context into my analysis?

⑨ Developing a critical writing style

This unit will help you to express your ideas about Macbeth as clearly and precisely as possible. The skills you will build are to:

- select vocabulary to express your ideas precisely
- link your ideas to express them clearly
- extend your sentences to develop ideas more fully.

In the exam you will face questions like the one below. This is about the extract on the next page. At the end of the unit you will **write one paragraph** in response to this question.

Exam-style question

Starting with this extract, how far do you think Shakespeare presents Macbeth as a good man who makes bad choices?

Write about:

- how Shakespeare presents Macbeth in this extract
- how Shakespeare presents Macbeth in the play as a whole.

(30 marks)

AO4 (4 marks)

Before you tackle the question you will work through three key questions in the **skills boosts** to help you develop a critical writing style.

 1 How do I choose vocabulary which expresses my ideas precisely?

 2 How can I link my ideas to express them more clearly?

 3 How can I extend my sentences to develop my ideas more fully?

Read the extract on the next page from Act 5 Scene 8 of *Macbeth*.

As you read, think about the following: ⊘

↓

What has happened before this scene? What happens after this scene?

Why does Macbeth choose to fight Macduff?

How have Macbeth's choices brought him to this situation?

Exam-style question

Read the following extract from Act 5 Scene 8 of *Macbeth* and then answer the question on page 65.

At this point in the play, Macbeth fights Macduff.

Extract A | Act 5 Scene 8 of *Macbeth*

> **MACDUFF**
> Turn, hell-hound, turn!
> **MACBETH**
> Of all men else I have avoided thee:
> But get thee back; my soul is too much charged
> With blood of thine already.
> **MACDUFF**
> 5   I have no words:
> My voice is in my sword: thou bloodier villain
> Than terms can give thee out!
> *They fight*
> **MACBETH**
> Thou losest labour:
> As easy mayst thou the intrenchant air
> 10 With thy keen sword impress as make me bleed:
> Let fall thy blade on vulnerable crests;
> I bear a charmed life, which must not yield,
> To one of woman born.
> **MACDUFF**
> Despair thy charm;
> 15 And let the angel whom thou still hast served
> Tell thee, Macduff was from his mother's womb
> Untimely ripp'd.
> **MACBETH**
> Accursed be that tongue that tells me so,
> For it hath cow'd my better part of man!
> 20 And be these juggling fiends no more believed,
> That palter with us in a double sense;
> That keep the word of promise to our ear,
> And break it to our hope. I'll not fight with thee.
> **MACDUFF**
> Then yield thee, coward,
> 25 And live to be the show and gaze o' the time:
> We'll have thee, as our rarer monsters are,
> Painted on a pole, and underwrit,
> 'Here may you see the tyrant.'
> **MACBETH**
> I will not yield,
> 30 To kiss the ground before young Malcolm's feet,
> And to be baited with the rabble's curse.
> Though Birnam wood be come to Dunsinane,
> And thou opposed, being of no woman born,
> Yet I will try the last. Before my body
> 35 I throw my warlike shield. Lay on, Macduff,
> And damn'd be him that first cries, 'Hold, enough!'

1 How do I choose vocabulary which expresses my ideas precisely?

You need to choose precise vocabulary to describe your response to the play as fully and accurately as possible.

1 How would you describe Shakespeare's presentation of these key characters at **each** of these points in the play?

Macbeth	
1.7 tries to halt the plan to kill Duncan	
1.7 is persuaded to kill Duncan	
2.1 expresses doubts about killing Duncan	
2.2 kills Duncan	
2.2 is filled with guilt and remorse for murder	
4.2 has Macduff's family killed	

Lady Macbeth	
	1.5 calls upon 'spirits' to fill her with cruelty
	1.5 persuades her husband to murder Duncan
	1.7 questions Macbeth's masculinity
	2.2 has drunk alcohol to make her 'bold'
	2.2 returns blood-stained daggers to king's chamber
	5.1 sleepwalks

Choose **two** words from the list below and write 🖉 them next to the relevant point in the play. Aim to choose words that describe your response as precisely as possible. You could choose two words with a similar meaning, or two very different words expressing different possible responses.

desperate	persuasive	brave	worried	cowardly	insincere
cruel	manipulative	decisive	unstable	fearful	deceitful
ambitious	cunning	devoted	troubled	vulnerable	hypocritical
ruthless	powerful	loyal	disturbed	submissive	duplicitous
evil	dominant	strong	mad	impotent	delusional

2 Now think about Shakespeare's intention: how did he want the audience to respond to these characters at these points in the play? Choose **one** or **two** of the words below and add 🖉 them to each of the key points in the play in question 1.

excitement	disappointment	revulsion	fear	admiration
anticipation	relief	disgust	shock	sorrow
tension	concern	anger	confusion	sympathy

➁ How can I link my ideas to express them more clearly?

You can use conjunctions to link your ideas, helping you to express your ideas more clearly and fluently.

| **Coordinating conjunctions** link related or contrasting ideas:

| and | | but | | or | | so | | **Subordinating conjunctions** express more complex connections:

• an explanation, e.g. | because | | in order to |

• a comparison, e.g. | although | | whereas |

• a sequence, e.g. | when | | after | | until | |

➀ Look at these pairs of sentences.

A

☐ Macbeth meets the witches. They make three predictions.

☐ Macbeth is unsure about murdering Duncan. Lady Macbeth has no doubts at all.

☐ Macbeth feels some loyalty to Duncan. He has just made him Thane of Cawdor.

B

☐ When Macbeth meets the witches, they make three predictions.

☐ Macbeth is unsure about murdering Duncan whereas Lady Macbeth has no doubts at all.

☐ Macbeth feels some loyalty to Duncan because he has just made him Thane of Cawdor.

a Circle Ⓐ the **conjunctions** in the sentences labelled B.

b Tick ✓ the version of each sentence that you feel is most clearly and fluently expressed.

➁ Rewrite 🖉 these pairs of sentences, using a conjunction to link them. Remember to choose and position your conjunction carefully to express each idea as clearly and fluently as possible.

| Lady Macbeth receives a letter from Macbeth. | **+** | She calls upon 'spirits' to fill her with cruelty. |

....

....

| Lady Macbeth is manipulative. | **+** | Macbeth makes the decision to murder Duncan. |

....

....

| Macbeth feels guilt at the murder of Duncan. | **+** | He shows none at the killing of Macduff's family. |

....

....

3 **How can I extend my sentences to develop my ideas more fully?**

One way to extend your sentences, and develop your ideas, is by using conjunctions. Other ways include:
- using present participles: a verb ending in *–ing*
- using the pronoun *which*.

Conjunctions	and	but	when	as	before	after
	although	if	whereas	unless	because	since

You could complete this sentence:

> Macbeth chooses to visit the witches...

- using this conjunction: → (after) the disturbing appearance of Banquo's ghost.

- or a present participle: → (believing) that they will reveal his fate.

- or *which*: → (which) results in his mistaken belief that he is invincible.

1 Complete ✏ this sentence in three different ways.

> Macbeth believes the witches' predictions...

a Use a conjunction: ....

b Use a present participle: ....

c Use *which*: ....

You can use *which* or a present participle to avoid repeatedly beginning sentences with
'This suggests...' or 'This shows...'.

For example:

> Macbeth is easily persuaded. (This suggests) he is weak.

> Macbeth is easily persuaded (which suggests) he is weak.

> Macbeth is easily persuaded, (suggesting) he is weak.

2 Change ✏ these sentences to make them a single sentence, using a present participle or *which*.

> Lady Macbeth seems to have total control. <u>This encourages</u> the audience to see Macbeth as powerless.

> Macbeth chooses to murder Banquo without Lady Macbeth's influence. <u>This creates</u> the impression that he is becoming more independent and more ruthless.

Developing a critical writing style

To express your ideas clearly and precisely, you can:

- select vocabulary that expresses your ideas precisely
- link your ideas using conjunctions, present participles, etc. to develop and express them clearly.

Now look at this exam-style question you saw on page 65.

Exam-style question

Starting with this extract, how far do you think Shakespeare presents Macbeth as a good man who makes bad choices?

Write about:

- how Shakespeare presents Macbeth in this extract
- how Shakespeare presents Macbeth in the play as a whole.

(1) Look at a short paragraph from one student's response to the question.

> At the start of the play Macbeth is presented as good and strong. He fights successfully in battle for King Duncan. He is described as 'brave'. He goes home to Lady Macbeth. She starts telling him to murder Duncan. This suggests that it is Lady Macbeth who makes her husband make bad choices. It gives the impression that Macbeth is good but weak.

a   Underline (A) **at least three** examples of vocabulary which could be more precise.

b   Note (✏) down in the margin **at least three** alternative vocabulary choices for each one.

c   Highlight (✏) any of the sentences which you feel should be linked or developed to improve the clarity and precision of the writing.

d   Write (✏) an improved version of this paragraph, either by adjusting the text above or by rewriting it in the space below.

....

....

....

....

....

....

Your turn!

You are now going to **write one paragraph** in response to the exam-style question.

Exam-style question

Starting with this extract, how far do you think Shakespeare presents Macbeth as a good man who makes bad choices?

Write about:
• how Shakespeare presents Macbeth in this extract
• how Shakespeare presents Macbeth in the play as a whole.

(30 marks)
AO4 (4 marks)

1 **a** Think about some of the things that Macbeth does, then decide what kind of choice he has made in each case. ✓

Macbeth...	Good choice?	Bad choice?	No choice?
• fights in battle	☐	☐	☐
• believes the witches' first three predictions	☐	☐	☐
• is persuaded to murder Duncan	☐	☐	☐
• has Banquo killed	☐	☐	☐
• decides to visit the witches	☐	☐	☐
• believes the witches' second three predictions	☐	☐	☐
• has Macduff's family murdered	☐	☐	☐
• fights Macduff	☐	☐	☐

b Choose **one** or **two** of the key events from the play which you can explore in your response to the exam-style question. You could choose from the list above, or use your own ideas. Note 🖉 them on paper.

c Look at each of your chosen events: how is Macbeth presented? Is he a good man? Has he made a bad choice? Why did he make it? How has Shakespeare created that impression? Add 🖉 your ideas to your notes.

d Use your ideas to write 🖉 a paragraph in response to the exam-style question on paper.

Hint: Remember to:
• choose your vocabulary carefully
• think about ways in which you can link your ideas to develop and express them clearly and precisely

Review your skills

Check up

Review your response to the exam-style question on page 71. Tick ✓ the column to show how well you think you have done each of the following.

	Not quite ✓	Nearly there ✓	Got it! ✓
selected precise vocabulary	☐	☐	☐
linked and developed my ideas clearly and precisely using conjunctions, present participles, etc.	☐	☐	☐

Look over all of your work in this unit. Note ✐ down the **three** most important things to remember when trying to express your ideas as clearly and precisely as possible.

1. ....

2. ....

3. ....

Need more practice?

You can EITHER:

(1) Look again at your paragraph written in response to the exam-style question on page 71. Rewrite ✐ it, experimenting with different vocabulary choices and sentence structures, linking your ideas in different ways. Which are most effective in expressing your ideas clearly and precisely?

AND/OR:

(2) Choose a **second** point from the suggestions on page 71. Write ✐ a further paragraph in response to the exam-style question, focusing closely on your vocabulary choice and sentence structures.

How confident do you feel about each of these **skills?** Colour ✐ in the bars.

(1) How do I choose vocabulary which expresses my ideas precisely?

(2) How can I link my ideas to express them more clearly?

(3) How can I extend my sentences to develop my ideas more fully?

More practice questions

Units 1 and 2

Exam-style question

Read the following extract from Act 1 Scene 2 of *Macbeth* and then answer the question that follows.

At this point in the play, a Captain has returned from the battlefield, describing how Macbeth helped Duncan's army to win a great victory over the invading Norwegian army.

Extract A | Act 1 Scene 2 of *Macbeth*

> **MALCOLM**
> This is the sergeant
> Who like a good and hardy soldier fought
> 'Gainst my captivity. Hail, brave friend!
> Say to the king the knowledge of the broil
> 5   As thou didst leave it.
> **CAPTAIN**
> Doubtful it stood;
> As two spent swimmers, that do cling together
> And choke their art. The merciless Macdonwald--
> Worthy to be a rebel, for to that
> 10   The multiplying villanies of nature
> Do swarm upon him--from the western isles
> Of kerns and gallowglasses is supplied;
> And fortune, on his damned quarrel smiling,
> Show'd like a rebel's whore. But all's too weak:
> 15   For brave Macbeth–well he deserves that name–
> Disdaining fortune, with his brandish'd steel,
> Which smoked with bloody execution,
> Like valour's minion carved out his passage
> Till he faced the slave;
> 20   Which ne'er shook hands, nor bade farewell to him,
> Till he unseam'd him from the nave to the chops,
> And fix'd his head upon our battlements.
> **DUNCAN**
> O valiant cousin! worthy gentleman!

Starting with this extract, explain how far you think Shakespeare presents Macbeth as a ruthless and violent man.

Write about:

• how Shakespeare presents Macbeth in this extract

• how Shakespeare presents Macbeth in the play as a whole.

(30 marks)

AO4 (4 marks)

Unit 1) Which key events in the play would you choose to write ✎ about in your response to this question?

Unit 2) Write ✎ **one** or **two** paragraphs in response to this question, focusing on the extract only.

Units 3 and 4

Read the following extract from Act 3 Scene 1 of *Macbeth* and then answer the question that follows.

At this point in the play, Macbeth has murdered Duncan and become King of Scotland. Macbeth is now planning to murder his friend, Banquo.

Extract B | Act 3 Scene 1 of *Macbeth*

Enter BANQUO

BANQUO
Thou hast it now: king, Cawdor, Glamis, all,
As the weird women promised, and, I fear,
Thou play'dst most foully for't: yet it was said
It should not stand in thy posterity,
5   But that myself should be the root and father
Of many kings. If there come truth from them--
As upon thee, Macbeth, their speeches shine--
Why, by the verities on thee made good,
May they not be my oracles as well,
10 And set me up in hope? But hush! no more.

Sennet sounded. Enter MACBETH, as king, LADY MACBETH, as queen, LENNOX, ROSS, Lords, Ladies, and Attendants

MACBETH
Here's our chief guest.
LADY MACBETH
If he had been forgotten,
It had been as a gap in our great feast,
And all-thing unbecoming.
MACBETH
15 Tonight we hold a solemn supper sir,
And I'll request your presence.
BANQUO
Let your Highness
Command upon me; to the which my duties
Are with a most indissoluble tie
20 For ever knit.
MACBETH
Ride you this afternoon?
BANQUO
Ay, my good lord.
MACBETH
We should have else desired your good advice,
Which still hath been both grave and prosperous,
25 In this day's council; but we'll take tomorrow.

Starting with this extract, explain how far you think Shakespeare explores the consequences of dishonesty and deception in *Macbeth*.

Write about:

- how Shakespeare presents Banquo and Macbeth as dishonest and deceitful in this extract
- how Shakespeare presents the consequences of dishonesty and deception in the play as a whole.

(30 marks)
AO4 (4 marks)

Unit 3 Write ✏ **one** or **two** paragraphs in response to this question, focusing on the extract only.

Unit 4 Write ✏ **two** paragraphs in response to this question, focusing on the second bullet point: the play as a whole.

Exam-style question

Read the following extract from Act 3 Scene 2 of *Macbeth* and then answer the question that follows.

At this point in the play, Macbeth and Lady Macbeth are about to attend a banquet celebrating Macbeth becoming King of Scotland. Lady Macbeth advises her husband that he must show his guests a false appearance of happiness.

Extract C | Act 3 Scene 2 of *Macbeth*

LADY MACBETH
Nought's had, all's spent,
Where our desire is got without content:
'Tis safer to be that which we destroy
Than by destruction dwell in doubtful joy.

Enter MACBETH

5   How now, my lord! why do you keep alone,
Of sorriest fancies your companions making,
Using those thoughts which should indeed have died
With them they think on? Things without all remedy
Should be without regard: what's done is done.
MACBETH
10   We have scotch'd the snake, not kill'd it:
She'll close and be herself, whilst our poor malice
Remains in danger of her former tooth.
But let the frame of things disjoint, both the worlds suffer,
Ere we will eat our meal in fear and sleep
15   In the affliction of these terrible dreams
That shake us nightly: better be with the dead,
Whom we, to gain our peace, have sent to peace,
Than on the torture of the mind to lie
In restless ecstasy. Duncan is in his grave;
20   After life's fitful fever he sleeps well;
Treason has done his worst: nor steel, nor poison,
Malice domestic, foreign levy, nothing,
Can touch him further.
LADY MACBETH
Come on;
25   Gentle my lord, sleek o'er your rugged looks;
Be bright and jovial among your guests tonight.
MACBETH
So shall I, love; and so, I pray, be you:
Let your remembrance apply to Banquo;
Present him eminence, both with eye and tongue:
30   Unsafe the while, that we
Must lave our honours in these flattering streams,
And make our faces vizards to our hearts,
Disguising what they are.
LADY MACBETH
You must leave this.
MACBETH
35   O, full of scorpions is my mind, dear wife!
Thou know'st that Banquo, and his Fleance, lives.

Starting with this extract, explore how Shakespeare presents false appearances in *Macbeth*.

Write about:
• the false appearances that Macbeth and Lady Macbeth show and talk about in this extract
• how Shakespeare presents false appearances in the play as a whole.   **(30 marks)**
                 AO4 (4 marks)

Unit 5 Plan 🖉 your response to this question.

Unit 6 Write 🖉 your response to this question.

Exam-style question

Read the following extract from Act 4 Scene 3 of *Macbeth* and then answer the question that follows.

At this point in the play Macduff learns that Macbeth has had his family murdered.

Extract D | Act 4 Scene 3 of *Macbeth*

> **ROSS**
> Your castle is surprised; your wife and babes
> Savagely slaughter'd: to relate the manner,
> Were, on the quarry of these murder'd deer,
> To add the death of you.
> **MALCOLM**
> 5 Merciful heaven!
> What, man! Ne'er pull your hat upon your brows;
> Give sorrow words: the grief that does not speak
> Whispers the o'er-fraught heart and bids it break.
> **MACDUFF**
> My children too?
> **ROSS**
> 10 Wife, children, servants, all
> That could be found.
> **MACDUFF**
> And I must be from thence!
> My wife kill'd too?
> **ROSS**
> I have said.
> **MALCOLM**
> 15 Be comforted:
> Let's make us medicines of our great revenge,
> To cure this deadly grief.
> **MACDUFF**
> He has no children. All my pretty ones?
> Did you say all? O hell-kite! All?
> 20 What, all my pretty chickens and their dam
> At one fell swoop?
> **MALCOLM**
> Dispute it like a man.
> **MACDUFF**
> I shall do so;
> But I must also feel it as a man:
> 25 I cannot but remember such things were,
> That were most precious to me. Did heaven look on,
> And would not take their part? Sinful Macduff,
> They were all struck for thee! naught that I am,
> Not for their own demerits, but for mine,
> 30 Fell slaughter on their souls. Heaven rest them now!
> **MALCOLM**
> Be this the whetstone of your sword: let grief
> Convert to anger; blunt not the heart, enrage it.

Starting with this extract, explore how Shakespeare presents violence and death in *Macbeth*.

Write about:

• how Shakespeare presents the impact of violence and death at this moment in the play

• how Shakespeare presents violence and death in the play as a whole.

(30 marks)

AO4 (4 marks)

Unit 7 Plan 🖉 your response to the question.

Unit 8

Exam-style question

Read the following extract from Act 5 Scene 3 of *Macbeth* and then answer the question that follows.

At this point in the play, Macbeth has learned that Malcolm and the English army are approaching, and that his Thanes have all deserted him. He calls for his loyal servant, Seyton.

Extract E | Act 5 Scene 3 of *Macbeth*

MACBETH
Bring me no more reports; let them fly all:
Till Birnam wood remove to Dunsinane,
I cannot taint with fear. What's the boy Malcolm?
Was he not born of woman? The spirits that know
5   All mortal consequences have pronounced me thus:
'Fear not, Macbeth; no man that's born of woman
Shall e'er have power upon thee.' Then fly, false thanes,
And mingle with the English epicures:
The mind I sway by and the heart I bear
10 Shall never sag with doubt nor shake with fear.

Enter a Servant

The devil damn thee black, thou cream-faced loon!
Where got'st thou that goose look?
Servant
There is ten thousand--
MACBETH
Geese, villain!
Servant
15 Soldiers, sir.
MACBETH
Go prick thy face, and over-red thy fear,
Thou lily-liver'd boy. What soldiers, patch?
Death of thy soul! those linen cheeks of thine
Are counsellors to fear. What soldiers, whey-face?
Servant
20 The English force, so please you.
MACBETH
Take thy face hence.

Exit Servant

Seyton!–I am sick at heart,
When I behold–Seyton, I say!–This push
Will cheer me ever, or disseat me now.
25 I have lived long enough: my way of life
Is fall'n into the sear, the yellow leaf;
And that which should accompany old age,
As honour, love, obedience, troops of friends,
I must not look to have; but, in their stead,
30 Curses, not loud but deep, mouth-honour, breath,
Which the poor heart would fain deny, and dare not.

Starting with this extract, explain how far you think Shakespeare presents Macbeth as a brave and heroic man.

Write about:

- how Shakespeare presents Macbeth in this extract
- how Shakespeare presents Macbeth in the play as a whole.

(30 marks)
AO4 (4 marks)

Unit 8 Write your response to this question.

Answers

Unit 1

Page 3

(1) Macbeth, Lady Macbeth, Banquo, Lady Macduff, Boy (son of Macduff), Duncan, Duncan's guards, Young Siward.

(2) Twice.

(3) (a) Three witches appear on stage. This is followed by news of Scotland's victory in battle against the invading Norwegian army.

(b) Macduff kills Macbeth and Malcolm is made King of Scotland.

(c) Duncan's army repels the invading Norwegian army.

Macbeth and Banquo meet the witches.

Macbeth kills King Duncan.

Macbeth kills Duncan's guards.

Macbeth has Banquo murdered.

Macbeth visits the witches.

Macbeth has Lady Macduff and her son murdered.

Lady Macbeth dies.

Macbeth kills Young Siward.

Macduff kills Macbeth.

Malcolm is King of Scotland.

Page 4

(1) (a) Causes: Macbeth hears the witches' predictions; Macbeth is made Thane of Cawdor (prompting him to believe the witches' predictions); Lady Macbeth persuades Macbeth to kill King Duncan.

(b) Consequences: Macbeth is King of Scotland; Macbeth has Banquo murdered; Macduff kills Macbeth.

Page 5

(1) Arguably, Macbeth would be made Thane of Cawdor; Duncan would remain as King, and be succeeded by Malcolm on his (natural) death.

(2) (b) Possible answers include:

- Macbeth is made Thane of Cawdor: Macbeth might have dismissed the witches' predictions and not acted upon them.

- Lady Macbeth persuades Macbeth: Macbeth might have been tempted, but ultimately have decided not, to kill Duncan.

- Macbeth murders King Duncan: the plot might have then focused more closely on Macbeth's relationship with his wife as she tried and failed to persuade him to kill Duncan.

- Macbeth has Macduff's wife and children murdered: Macduff might not have agreed to, and led, the fight against Macbeth.

Page 6

This student has effectively placed the extract in the context of the whole play, considered its impact, and used that to come to a conclusion: Shakespeare presents the supernatural as a powerful influence on Macbeth.

The student has selected relevant evidence and focused on the implications of the characters' lines and of Shakespeare's language choices.

Page 7

(1) (a) 1.3; 3.4; 4.1

(b) Arguably, 1.3; 4.1 (although it is the appearance of Banquo's ghost in 3.4 that drives Macbeth to seek out the witches in 4.1)

(c) 2.2; 3.3; 4.1; 4.2; 5.8

(d) 1.5–1.7

Page 8

Responses could focus on:

- Macbeth's doubts and indecision in:
  - Act 1 Scene 3 ('If chance will have me king, why, chance may crown me / Without my stir.')
  - Act 1 Scene 7 ('We will proceed no further…')
  - Act 2 Scene 1 (He sees a dagger).
- Macbeth's guilt in:
  - Act 2 Scene 2 (following the murder of Duncan)
  - Act 3 Scene 4 (in the appearance of Banquo's ghost).
- Macbeth's ruthless use of violence in:
  - murdering Duncan, Banquo, and Macduff's family.

Unit 2

Page 11

(1) (a) 1(A), 2(B), 6(C) are arguably the most relevant.

(b) A: Macbeth clearly respects Duncan's power and, perhaps, feels the need to clearly show this. It could suggest that those in power demand such shows.

B: It suggests that those who show respect and loyalty are rewarded by those in power.

C: It suggests that power can be tempting, and that it can be threatened by those who are tempted.

Page 12

(1) (a) Duncan has rewarded Macbeth for his loyalty and will reward him again. Duncan shows his gratitude to Banquo as well.

(b) Duncan is, perhaps, demonstrating that those who are loyal will be rewarded. The implication is that Duncan wants his men to respect, and be loyal to, his position of power.

(c) Duncan clearly recognises the need to keep his subjects' loyalty, particularly following the execution of the treacherous Thane of Cawdor. This could suggest that an effective leader recognises that, once gained, power must be nurtured and maintained.

(d) For example: 'I have begun to plant thee, and will labour / To make thee full of growing.'; 'Let me infold thee / And hold thee to my heart.'

Page 13

(1) All are valid.

(2) Examples:

B, A, D, C, E, F

E, F, C, D, A, B

(3) <u>For example:</u> [E] Shakespeare does not always present power as destructive in 'Macbeth'.

<u>In the extract</u> [A] King Duncan is presented as warm, generous and grateful for Macbeth and Banquo's victory over the Norwegian army.

<u>For example,</u> [C] Duncan tells Macbeth that he will 'labour / To make thee full of growing', suggesting that Duncan will reward him with more honours and titles if he remains loyal and fights hard for Duncan.

<u>Similarly,</u> [D] Duncan calls Banquo 'Noble' and embraces him: 'Let me infold thee / And hold thee to my heart', suggesting he feels respect and affection for him.

<u>This shows that</u> [B] Duncan uses his power in a positive way, rewarding his people for their help and support.

<u>It suggests that</u> [F] power can be constructive, not destructive, if the king does not take his power, and the people he has power over, for granted.

(4) **(a)** Key point: A

(b) Evidence: C, D

(c) Comment: B

(d) Response: E, F

Page 14

(1) **(a)** The student has achieved all of the criteria.

(b) Key point: *In this extract, King Duncan appears to be a good leader, using his power to reward those who are loyal to him and fight for him.*

Evidence: *Macbeth has returned victorious from battle, and has been rewarded for his loyalty with the title of Thane of Cawdor. Duncan seems to promise that Macbeth will continue to be rewarded more if he continues to please Duncan: 'I have begun to plant thee, and will labour / To make thee full of growing.'*

Comment: *While this seems to be a perfect picture of a loyal subject and a grateful king, it could be argued that Duncan is bribing Macbeth with the title of Thane of Cawdor to make sure he stays loyal. Furthermore, this extract comes just after Duncan has had the previous Thane of Cawdor executed for treachery.*

Response: *So this part of the play suggests that, in order to keep power, you must repay loyalty, but be cruel and ruthless when your power is challenged.*

Page 16

Responses could focus on:

- Macbeth described as 'brave' by the Captain, and 'valiant' by Duncan, suggesting his positive qualities are recognised and respected at this point in the play

- Macbeth's violent and ruthless attack on Macdonwald described in graphic detail: his sword 'smoked with bloody execution'; 'unseam'd him... fix'd his head upon our battlements...'.

Unit 3

Page 19

(1) **(a)** Examples could include: 'Great', 'worthy', 'Greater'.

(b) This could suggest that Lady Macbeth is impressed by, and admires, her husband's achievements, and/or believes that she is able to influence and manipulate his actions both through flattery and by highlighting the inevitable course of events that the witches predicted.

(2) A:

(a) **i** Look innocent; be ruthless.

ii She fears her husband's appearance will reveal his plans; to encourage his resolve.

(b)/(c) Imperatives 'Look', 'be' suggest her dominance and control; 'flower', 'serpent' suggest her reliance on deceit and ruthlessness.

B:

(a) **i** Look innocent and I will take care of everything else.

ii To calm his fears; to assert her dominance.

(b)/(c) Imperatives 'Look', 'leave' suggest her dominance and control; the euphemism 'the rest', referring to the regicide she plans, suggests her manipulation of Macbeth's thoughts and feelings.

Page 20

(1) **(a)** All are valid.

(b) Short lines, delivered at speed, might contribute to these moods.

(2) **(a)** Macbeth says much less than Lady Macbeth; Lady Macbeth does most of the talking.

(b) Macbeth is, perhaps, anxious; Lady Macbeth's excitement and insistence dominate the scene and her husband.

Page 21

(1) All are valid.

(2) The imperatives 'Look' and 'be' begin these abrupt commands, suggesting Lady Macbeth's emphatic dominance of her husband; the contrast of 'flower' and 'serpent' in these abrupt commands emphasises the deceit that her ambitions demand of him.

Page 22

key point focusing on the key words in the question	As soon as Macbeth appears at the start of the extract, Lady Macbeth ruthlessly dominates the scene and tries to influence him.
evidence from the text to support your point	She welcomes him home, calling him 'Great Glamis! worthy Cawdor!'
comments on the evidence and its impact	These short, emphatic exclamations suggest her excitement and are meant to flatter Macbeth. She uses the positive adjectives 'great' and 'worthy' to boost his confidence and make him feel important. She also uses his new title of 'Cawdor' to remind him of the witches' prediction that has already come true, and the rest of the prediction which she wants him to make come true.
a response to the question	Lady Macbeth doubts her husband will be ruthless enough to do this, and so feels she must flatter and manipulate him to be as ruthless and ambitious as she is.
a comment on language choice(s)	She uses the positive adjectives 'great' and 'worthy' to boost his confidence and make him feel important. She also uses his new title of 'Cawdor' to remind him of the witches' prediction that has already come true, and the rest of the prediction which she wants him to make come true.
a comment on structural choice(s)	These short, emphatic exclamations suggest her excitement and are meant to flatter Macbeth.

Page 24

Responses could focus on:

- Banquo clearly suspects Macbeth but says nothing to him
- Macbeth intends to murder Banquo but flatters him as 'our chief guest'
- Macbeth questions Banquo about his plans, claiming to be in need of 'good advice'; perhaps, though, wanting the information to pass on to Banquo's murderers.

Unit 4

Page 27

1. brave, dishonest, ambitious, superstitious, frightened
2. For example: ruthless, unstable, unemotional, unpredictable
3. All responses are arguable; each key scene marks a step in the hardening of Macbeth to the demands of his ruthless ambition.

Page 28

1. For example:

Power: 1.4: Duncan shows his power; Macbeth considers what he must do to acquire it.

Ambition: 1.5: Lady Macbeth expresses her ambitions, and fears that Macbeth does not have the ruthlessness needed to achieve them.

Violence: 2.2: the aftermath of the murder of Duncan.

The supernatural: 3.4: the ghost of Banquo appears to Macbeth.

Loyalty: 1.4: Thane of Cawdor is hanged for treachery; Macbeth is rewarded for his loyalty while secretly planning treachery.

2. a. For example: necessary, a great responsibility, corrupting and dangerous.

   b. The role of king is clearly valued in the play; however, it seems potentially dangerous for those in power, and corrupting for those who seek power.

Page 29

1. a. … in Act 1 Scene 5, she calls upon 'spirits' to 'fill' her with 'direst cruelty'.

   … in Act 5 Scene 1, she sleepwalks, clearly troubled by guilt.

   … we are told that she has died, it is suggested 'by self and violent hands' (5.8).

   b. Despite her initial, apparently ruthless, ambition, Lady Macbeth is increasingly troubled, and ultimately consumed, by guilt.

2. a. Statements B, C and D are arguable to an extent.

   b. For example: Violence is presented as a part of bravery in battle, and an appropriate punishment for treachery. In Macbeth's actions, unjustifiable violence is presented as counter-productive, leading to crippling guilt and more violence: 'blood will have blood'.

Page 30

1. a. The student refers to:

   1.4: Duncan praises Cawdor. Macbeth plots while Banquo is loyal.

   1.3: Macbeth and Banquo meet the witches.

   3.1: Banquo suspects Macbeth; Macbeth arranges Banquo's murder.

   b. Paragraph 1: *This shows him as deceitful and ungrateful and ruthless in his ambition for power. It is his selfishness and cold-blooded planning that make him seem so evil.*

   Paragraph 2: *… suggesting that evil is stronger than good, or perhaps that evil is very dangerous and that good must challenge and overcome it…*

   c. *This also contrasts with Banquo. … However, Banquo remains loyal to the king. … evil is very dangerous and that good must challenge and overcome it, which Banquo does not do…*

Page 32

Responses could focus on:

- Macbeth's deception of Duncan, plotting to murder him while Duncan honours him
- Lady Macbeth's deception of herself and of Macbeth: she is not as cold and cruel as she suggests, drinking alcohol in order to face the murder of Duncan, refusing to commit the murder herself because he resembles her father, expressing anxieties in Act 3, which become far more serious in Act 5 as she sleepwalks
- the witches' deception of Macbeth, their predictions in Act 4 leading him to believe he is invincible.

Unit 5

Page 35

1. a Lady Macbeth suggests that guilt can be avoided by simply not thinking about 'these deeds'. She fears that the guilt will lead to madness. Macbeth fears that his guilt will stop him from ever sleeping again.

   b For example: The reactions of both characters suggest the power of guilt to dominate, or even damage, the mind.

2. a/b All are arguably valid.

Page 36

1. a All are arguably valid.

   b For example:
      2.2: C, D, E
      3.2: A, B, C, D, E
      3.4: A, C, D
      4.2: B, C, E
      5.1: A, C, D
      5.8: E

2. Key points are likely to focus on Macbeth's initial but rapidly diminishing guilt and Lady Macbeth's dismissal of, then destruction by, guilt.

Page 37

1. A, D, C, B

2. a For example: A, C, B, D (i.e. focus first on Macbeth, then on Lady Macbeth)

   b For example: D, C, A, B (i.e. focus on the suppression of guilt, then the impact of guilt)

Page 38

1. a B
   b B

Page 40

Responses could focus on:

In the extract:

- Lady Macbeth expresses her anxieties to herself ('our desire is got without content'), then accuses Macbeth of similar anxiety ('thoughts which should indeed have died') and advises Macbeth to be 'bright and jovial'
- Macbeth tells his wife to present a false appearance to Banquo: 'present him eminence', knowing that he plans to have him killed.

In the play as a whole:

- the false appearance Macbeth and Lady Macbeth give to Duncan when they welcome him to their castle, knowing they will murder him
- Lady Macbeth's false appearance of cold cruelty, which soon falters and, eventually, destroys her
- the false appearance of the witches' predictions, promising greatness and invincibility, but bringing Macbeth's destruction.

Unit 6

Page 43

1. a This moment in the play reveals something **significant** about Macbeth and Lady Macbeth.

   b The themes of the supernatural, guilt, ~~power~~ and deception are all relevant to this moment.

2. a 3.1: Banquo, Macbeth; 3.2: Macbeth, Lady Macbeth

   b 3.1, 3.3

   c Scenes 1, 2 and 3 are the most significant scenes in Act 3, including scene 4.

3. a All are valid.

   b B and D are arguably the most significant, showing Lady Macbeth's manipulation of her husband.

   c All are valid.

   d For example: 'dash'd the brains out'.

Page 44

1. Key event: For example: Macbeth's irrational behaviour takes no account of the impression he is giving his Thanes.

   Key quotation: For example: 'Which of you have done this?'

2. Examples are likely to focus on Lady Macbeth's control of her husband; the witches' influence on Macbeth's choices and actions; the response of Macduff and Malcolm to Macbeth's actions.

3. D, E, G and H are all valid.

4. Using both key events and quotations is likely to be a more effective approach.

Page 45

1. All are valid.

2. For example:

   Macbeth has Macduff's family murdered in response to the witches' predictions in Act 4 Scene 1.

   It suggests Macbeth's ruthless desire to maintain his power, but his use of murderers also suggests he is still affected by the guilt of committing Duncan's murder himself.

   It suggests Macbeth is attempting to maintain control of his power, but is losing control of his judgement and morality.

   This murder of a woman and child is intended to shock and repulse the audience, destroying any remaining sympathy for Macbeth.

Page 46

uses a key event as evidence	He hears the witches' prediction that he will be King of Scotland and almost immediately begins to think about how he will make this prediction come true.
uses a quotation as evidence	He talks about his 'black and deep desires'
explains the context of the evidence	as he watches Duncan announce that Malcolm will be the next king.
analysis comments on the writer's choices of language and/or structure	Describing his ambitions as 'deep' suggests how strongly he feels them, and the word 'black' suggests that he knows they are wrong.
analysis comments on character	presenting Macbeth as a villain threatening to take control of the situation.
analysis comments on theme	At the beginning of the play, Macbeth appears to be in control of his destiny… However, it is not long before Macbeth becomes less sure of his 'desires' and is forced to let Lady Macbeth take control.
analysis comments on Shakespeare's intention	At this point Shakespeare is creating a sense of excitement for the audience

Page 48

Responses could focus on:

In the extract:

- Lady Macbeth expresses her anxieties to herself ('our desire is got without content'), then accuses Macbeth of similar anxiety ('thoughts which should indeed have died') and advises Macbeth to be 'bright and jovial'
- Macbeth tells his wife to present a false appearance to Banquo: 'present him eminence', knowing that he plans to have him killed.

In the play as a whole:

- the false appearance Macbeth and Lady Macbeth give to Duncan when they welcome him to their castle, knowing they will murder him
- Lady Macbeth's false appearance of cold cruelty, which soon falters and, eventually, destroys her
- the false appearance of the witches' predictions, promising greatness and invincibility, but bringing Macbeth's destruction.

Unit 7

Page 51

(1) For example:

Beginning: witches, battle, chaos, disorder, plotting, conflict, manipulation

Middle: murder, ghost, madness, evil

End: order, justice, peace, harmony

(2) a/b As Macbeth's power grows, so does his evil. Lady Macbeth's power and evil develop inversely, starting at a high level and ebbing as the play develops.

Page 52

(1) Establishing Macbeth's strengths of bravery and loyalty, then revealing his plotting, emphasises the influence of the witches.

(2) This sequence shows the progression of Macbeth's ruthlessness: from the murder of a friend, to the mass murder of a woman and her children. Shakespeare also uses the murder of his family to spur Macduff's revenge and bring about the death of Macbeth.

(3) The first set of predictions is soon proved true, convincing Macbeth of the witches' power; they exploit his trust in the second set of predictions, which leads to his destruction. The witches are a dramatic and exciting element of the play which Shakespeare makes the most of.

Page 53

(1) a All are valid, although A and B are weaker comments without the support of C and D to develop them.

(2) Comments may focus on comparing this murder with that of Banquo, and/or the consequences of the murder, spurring Macduff to revenge.

Page 54

(1) The relationship/development between the murder of Banquo and the murder of Macduff's family.

(2) shocking the audience by taking Macbeth's cruelty and violence a step further.

(3) It shows how low Macbeth has sunk and emphasises the power and evil influence of the witches' predictions.

Page 56

Key events could include:

- the battle described in Act 1 Scene 2 when Macbeth 'unseam'd' Macdonwald
- the murder of Duncan in Act 2 Scene 2
- the murders of Banquo and Macduff's family
- the death of Macbeth.

Key structural features could include:

- the description of the battle establishing Macbeth's reputation at the start of the play, which he soon loses
- the development of Macbeth's attitude to murder, moving from crippling guilt to cold acceptance.

Unit 8

Page 59

(1) All are relevant, apart from James I's publication A Counterblaste to Tobacco.

(2) The witches: 17th century attitudes to witchcraft

Lady Macbeth: 17th century attitudes to women and witchcraft

Macbeth/Murder of Duncan: The divine right of kings

Page 60

1. a. A identifies a relevant belief.

   B identifies the time in which the play was written, a relevant belief, Shakespeare's intention and its impact on an audience.

   C identifies the time in which the play was written, a relevant attitude, its impact on a contemporary and modern audience.

   b. B and C are the most detailed, developed comments on context.

2. a. Responses are likely to focus on the dramatic impact of this opening scene being heightened by a contemporary audience's fear of witchcraft.

Page 61

1. a. Sentences A–D focus on impact; Sentences a–d focus on context.

   b is relevant to A and B; a and d are relevant to C and D; c is arguably linked to D but very tenuously.

Page 62

uses a key event as evidence	When Lady Macbeth reads Macbeth's letter about the witches' predictions, she calls on the forces of evil
uses a quotation as evidence	to 'unsex' her and fill her with 'direst cruelty' so that she has the power to persuade her husband to murder Duncan.
comments on the impact of the evidence	This is a disturbing moment in the play for a modern audience as it suggests she is trying to overcome her conscience so that she can persuade Macbeth to commit murder.
identifies a relevant contextual point	However, because Shakespeare's audience firmly believed in 'spirits' and witches and the harm that they could do to normal human beings,
explores Shakespeare's intention in the light of this contextual point	Shakespeare wants his audience to be both shocked and disturbed by Lady Macbeth and even more so because this is her first appearance in the play.
explores the audience's response in the light of this contextual point	this would be a terrifying moment for them.

Page 64

Responses could focus on:

- Macbeth's bravery:
  - Macbeth's success in battle in Act 1 Scene 2
  - Macbeth's blind determination to fight Macduff, knowing his death is almost inevitable.
- Other, perhaps more apparent, aspects of his character:
  - his inability to deny his wife's persuasion or the witches' predictions
  - the guilt that threatens to halt his ambitions – which could be perceived as a weakness or a strength
  - his ruthless ambition in killing Duncan, Banquo and Macduff's family.

Unit 9

Page 67

1. Sample adjectives for Macbeth's scenes: brave, ambitious, ruthless, disturbed, submissive

   Sample adjectives for Lady Macbeth's scenes: ambitious, ruthless, decisive, disturbed, duplicitous, delusional

2. Sample adjectives for Macbeth's scenes: tension, concern, disappointment, revulsion, shock, sympathy

   Sample adjectives for Lady Macbeth's scenes: tension, concern, revulsion, shock, sympathy

Page 68

1. a. when, whereas, because

   b. All version 'B's use conjunctions to express the relationship between the two clauses more clearly.

2. For example:

   When Lady Macbeth receives a letter from Macbeth, she calls upon 'spirits' to fill her with cruelty.

   Although Lady Macbeth is manipulative, Macbeth makes the decision to murder Duncan.

   Macbeth feels guilt at the murder of Duncan but he shows none at the killing of Macduff's family.

Page 69

1. For example:

   a. Macbeth believes the witches' predictions and chooses to act on them.

   b. Macbeth believes the witches' predictions, misunderstanding their true meaning.

   c. Macbeth believes the witches' predictions, which is, perhaps, his poorest decision in the play.

2. For example:

   Lady Macbeth seems to have total control, which encourages the audience to see Macbeth as powerless.

   Macbeth chooses to murder Banquo without Lady Macbeth's influence, creating the impression that he is becoming more independent and more ruthless.

Page 70

1. a/b For example:

   good (loyal, brave, honourable); telling (persuading, encouraging, urging); makes (leads, encourages, forces); weak (impotent, submissive, powerless)

   c/d For example:

   At the start of the play Macbeth is presented as loyal and courageous. He fights successfully in battle for King Duncan and is described as 'brave'. When he goes home to Lady Macbeth, she starts persuading him to murder Duncan, which suggests that it is Lady Macbeth who leads her husband to make bad choices and gives the impression that Macbeth is good but impotent.

Notes